STO

FRIENDS
OF ACPL

W9-DIZ-276

3-18-68

MAN and the
CALIFORNIA
CONDOR

MAN and the
CALIFORNIA
CONDOR

The Embattled History and Uncertain Future of
North America's Largest Free-living Bird

by Ian McMillan

E. P. Dutton & Co., Inc. New York 1968

First Edition

Copyright © 1968 by Ian McMillan
All rights reserved. Printed in the U.S.A.

No part of this book may be reproduced in any form without permission in writing from the publisher, except by a reviewer who wishes to quote brief passages in connection with a review written for inclusion in a magazine, newspaper or broadcast.

Published simultaneously in Canada by Clarke, Irwin & Company Limited, Toronto and Vancouver

Library of Congress Catalog Card Number: 67-11374

Grateful acknowledgment is given to McNally & Loftin, Publishers, for permission to quote from *California Condor* by Dick Smith and Robert Easton.

Photographs numbered 1, 2, 4, 5, 8, 11, 12, 22, 23, 24, 25, 26 and 28 courtesy of Carl B. Koford; 3 and 6 courtesy of H. T. Bohlman and W. L. Finley from G. M. Christman, Museum of Vertebrate Zoology, Berkeley; 7 courtesy of John Borneman from National Audubon Society; 9 and 10 courtesy of Walter R. Spofford; 13 courtesy of William Dawson from National Audubon Society; 27 courtesy of the Los Angeles Zoo. All photographs not credited were taken by the author.

1458236

Acknowledgments

THE HELP I HAVE RECEIVED IN WRITING THIS BOOK SUS-
tains my belief that the condors and the people who
defend them are going to prevail. My wife May typed
the manuscript; Kenneth Millar, the novelist, gave freely
of his time and talent in various ways of correction
and rearrangement. Among others who gave help and
advice were Robert O. Easton, Dick Smith, Dr. Loye
Miller, Dr. Hildegarde Howard and Dr. Harvey I.
Fisher. Photographs have been freely made available by
G. M. Christman, Dr. Carl Koford and Dr. Walter
Spofford and also by the National Geographic Society
and the U.S. Bureau of Sport Fisheries and Wildlife.
To these and others who helped I am deeply indebted.

Contents

Illustrations

PHOTOGRAPHS

MAP

MAN and the
CALIFORNIA
CONDOR

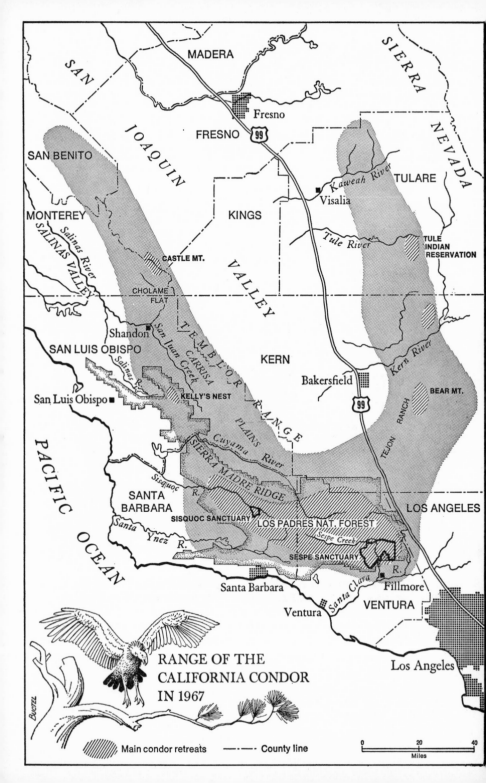

RANGE OF THE CALIFORNIA CONDOR IN 1967

//////// Main condor retreats — - — - County line

0   20   40
Miles

Chapter I

THE BACKGROUND

NORTHWARD FROM LOS ANGELES, IN SOUTH-
central California, is a special piece of country. It is a multicolored
mosaic of sweeping, semiarid grasslands and wooded uplands rising
into rugged, brush-covered mountains that rim the southern San
Joaquin Valley. This is the home range and the final retreat of the
California condor.

Perhaps it is the rarity of the condor that lends a mysterious
enchantment to the wilderness retreats over which the great birds
soar. In these secluded places the condor is a symbol of wildness.
The wilderness, with all its intangible meanings, seems to appear in
its most tangible form when a condor is sighted, soaring effortlessly
over some mountain stronghold.

In the 1940's, after an extensive field study, it was estimated that,
in all, about sixty condors were alive. The population had evidently

remained stable at around that number for at least the previous three decades. However, in a recent survey completed in 1964, the various counts showed an alarming decline from 1947. Only an estimated forty individuals remained. In seventeen years the critically endangered species had declined by a third. Wanton shooting appeared to be the main cause of the decline, but some of the loss had been caused by poison.

The condor is rare not only because its numbers are limited. Having an average wingspread of nine feet and a weight of twenty pounds, it is the largest free-living bird in North America. And its unique size is matched by an equal distinctiveness in behavior.

Strictly a scavenger, the condor never preys on living animals. It feeds only on carcasses found on the wide range over which it forages. Cattle and sheep are its main food, with carcasses of small calves the most common form of carrion. Dead deer also provide an important source of food. Various species of small mammals, mainly rodents and rabbits, are occasionally eaten by the big vultures.

The California condor is sometimes confused with another great vulture, a bird that inhabits the mountains and coastal regions of western South America. But the two species, although similar in size and resembling each other in some other ways, are not closely related. Furthermore, the South American, or Andean, condor is under no immediate threat of extinction.

Popular misinformation has represented the condor as a lingering, doomed relic of the geologic past, unable to cope with human civilization. The facts contradict this proposition. It is barbarism, not civilization, that threatens the rare birds. In spite of the laws protecting them today, the main threat to their survival is still a man with a gun. The central feature of any program to preserve the condor must be to stop the shooting of condors.

One of the first real acts of condor protection occurred in 1908 when a young condor was shot at a nest near Pasadena and the carcass was offered for sale. Learning of this, a group of young egg collectors in the area had the guilty person arrested. The man was fined fifty dollars, at that time a considerable penalty. This pioneering act of wildlife protection remains historic as the only case on record in which anyone killing a condor has been successfully prosecuted. It also confirms the paradox so often found in the history of the condor: The species has sometimes gained from what first appeared as adversity. Among the collectors who brought this guilty person to court, some had probably taken condor eggs.

These young egg collectors were leaders of the Cooper Ornithological Club, an organization named after an eminent naturalist of that time. Its official journal, *The Condor,* had rapidly grown to become the leading publication of western ornithology. By 1908, this scientific journal was already the main source of factual information on the condor.

Among the leaders of the Cooper Club in 1908 was a young naturalist who was already concerned about condor preservation. From his early boyhood on an Oklahoma Indian reservation, Joseph Grinnell had been interested in natural history. Going to California around 1890, he later entered Stanford University as a student in zoology. There he became associated with other young ornithologists who had organized the Cooper Club. In 1901, Grinnell was elected president of the organization. A few years later he became editor of *The Condor,* and held that post until his death in 1939.

In 1908, Grinnell moved to the University of California at Berkeley, and began building the Museum of Vertebrate Zoology. Under his continued direction this scientific institution became one of the world's outstanding centers of biological research and information. It became outstanding, also, as the guiding force of an organized program for the preservation of the California condor. In a conservation bulletin published in 1914, Grinnell expressed his attitude on the subject. "Our successors," he admonished, "will not approve of our thoughtlessness in completely destroying the California condor any less than we deplore the wanton destruction of the great auk by our ancestors."

Steadily, with increasing public interest in the condor, laws protecting the species became more stringent. Collecting of the birds and their eggs, which had been a common practice, was officially brought to a halt in the early 1920's.

In three decades of work at the University of California, as scientist, writer, and teacher, Joseph Grinnell became a leader in the world of natural science. Out of his classroom came a force of scientists, teachers, and administrators to spread the new gospel of conservation. Outstanding among these leaders was Alden Miller, who became a stalwart champion of condor preservation, and in 1939 succeeded Grinnell as Director of the Museum of Vertebrate

Zoology. When an official organized plan of condor preservation was at last put into operation in 1947, the new program was based on research conducted by this museum.

The research project had been initiated by the National Audubon Society through its president at that time, John H. Baker. In the middle 1930's a local controversy over the California condor had become national. Robert E. Easton, a militant and competent local conservationist, was adamantly opposing a road-building project that would have seriously affected a favorite wilderness retreat of the condors. Easton was manager of the big Sisquoc Ranch that lay across the main access route to the condor country of upper Sisquoc Canyon in the mountains of northeastern Santa Barbara County, a central part of Los Padres National Forest. A road that would have invaded this remote piece of condor territory was planned by the United States Forest Service. With the help of the Audubon Society, Easton fought successfully to prevent this construction, and as a result of the controversy a small section of the region was officially established as a condor sanctuary in 1937. This area of about 1,200 acres included a great cliff and waterfall where condors were known to roost and sometimes came to drink and bathe. Officially designated as the Sisquoc Condor Sanctuary, it has since remained closed to public use or travel.

This widely publicized controversy was of vital significance. By bringing the National Audubon Society into the immediate field of condor protection, it stirred the official administration of condor preservation out of a deplorable state of doldrums.

At the beginning of the Sisquoc dispute, the Forest Service evidently had practically no factual information on the status of the species. Nor did it evidently have funds available to conduct even a rough census of the condors then inhabiting the area. Since all the remaining condors were then thought to be confined to a region mainly within Los Padres National Forest, this lack of official information on the condor seems all the more significant.

The Audubon Society first became involved in the Sisquoc dispute in 1936. With factual information on the status of the condor seen as a necessity, the organization made available to the Forest Service the sum of $270 to cover the expense of a brief census. This sketchy count was made during a ten-day period by two of the forest guards. One was stationed in Sisquoc Canyon, the other near

Whiteacre Peak, some fifty airline miles to the southeast, where the Sespe Condor Refuge was later to be established.

From these counts it was estimated that forty-nine condors were then ranging the mountains of Ventura and Santa Barbara counties. Three years later, a second report was compiled by Cyril S. Robinson, Associate Forester. In this later report the population was estimated to number between fifty-five and sixty birds. The final statement of Robinson's report was a recommendation that a really satisfactory investigation of condor status would require a great deal more time and study. The Forest Service was now giving new and proper attention to the condor. Fred P. Cronemiller, its head biologist in the California region, was a strong conservationist.

The Sisquoc Sanctuary represents the first confrontation between the bulldozer and the forces of condor preservation. It stands as a working monument to the ecological proposition that to protect the condor its wilderness habitat must also be protected.

The dispute in the Sisquoc occurred, providentially, at a time when the bulldozer was first becoming a major implement of Forest Service administration and when the general policy of that agency was becoming oriented toward the development and promotion of a new bureaucratic resource called "use." Without the dramatic showdown in the Sisquoc, the condor might well have passed on, quietly and unnoticed, to join its recent associate, the California grizzly, in the limbo of extinction.

The Sisquoc region in recent years has not been frequented by the birds in such large numbers as in the late 1930's. However, the species still is regularly noted in the area, and there is evidence that the historic habitat may be in continued use as nesting territory.

In 1939, recognizing the obvious need for further condor research, John Baker, of the Audubon Society, took the problem to Joseph Grinnell and his top associate at the Museum of Vertebrate Zoology, Alden Miller. Out of this meeting the society entered into a cooperative undertaking with the University of California in which Grinnell and Miller would plan and direct a study of the life history and general status of the condor over a three-year period.

The person finally selected to do this research was Carl Koford, a graduate student at the Museum of Vertebrate Zoology. He was already a trained zoologist and forester. In March of 1939 the fieldwork began.

Most of Koford's fieldwork was done in Ventura County, in the area that was later established as the Sespe Condor Sanctuary. The Forest Service constructed a small lookout building on a strategic high point. From this lookout the young researcher spent many days with binoculars and telescope, watching condor activity and locating nesting sites.

To do his research, Koford found it necessary at times practically to live with the condors, watching them daily and for hours at a time. He also made important observations that did not directly involve condors. Once, as he was quietly watching from the top of a high peak, Koford saw a mountain lion stalking a herd of deer. The deer, he noted, were in a "greenish brown meadow, about a quarter-mile square in area and of about 20 percent slope. . . . There was a southwest breeze. . . . The sky was clear and the temperature was about 50 F. . . . The cat seemed to be stalking the deer patiently, alternately walking a short distance and stopping for from one to five minutes as if to watch them. . . . In walking, the lion main-tained a steady pace of about two steps per second regardless of slope and carried the tail and head low. . . . Frequently the cat sat erect, raising the head as high as it seemed possible; but at least twice it lay flat on the ground, apparently on its side. . . . This meadow may be a frequent hunting ground for lions, as I have observed up to 60 deer there and have often found lion tracks in the vicinity."

I include these details to show the precise and inclusive method of Koford's study. But it is important also to indicate the other things that can be seen when people look for condors.

Koford's study focused on the nesting and roosting behavior of the condors. By 1946, all the known nesting places were within a strip, 400 miles long and 40 miles wide, reaching from Santa Cruz County to San Diego County. In 1950, however, a nest was dis-covered in a big tree in the mountains of Tulare County, 120 miles from the coast. With the exception of this surprising nest in the hollow of a big tree, all others that Koford investigated were either in rock cliffs or among boulders. Some were in the faces of high, precipitous cliffs; others, which a man could reach without using a rope, were located on steep, rocky slopes. One site was a cave 20 feet in length, with an entrance 10 feet by 12 feet. Some nests were in cavities barely large enough for the two adult condors to enter at once.

The survival of all bird species depends primarily on the success of the nesting cycle. In the condor this period covers at least a full year and part of the next. The time that the cycle begins may vary over two months. In one nest that Koford watched, the egg was laid on March 23. Condor eggs have been collected as early as February and as late as May.

Following an important period of nest selection and egg-laying, incubation lasts at least forty-two days. The nestling stage continues for about five months, after which the juvenile leaves the nest but is unable to fly for at least another two months. For a few months after this, the young condor, although able to fly and get some of its own food, is still fed at times by the parents. Condors feed their young by regurgitation. Observers have seen juveniles well into their second year of growth being fed by adult birds. Both of the parent birds share in the duties of incubation and feeding of the young. There is no evidence that a pair of condors has ever successfully nested more than once in two years.

After becoming independent of its parents, a young condor does not reach full maturity and breeding age until it is about six years old. This, together with the single egg and the two-year nesting cycle, causes the species to have one of the lowest rates of reproduction found in birds.

Perches consisting of rocks, ledges, trees, or shrubs near the nest were found to be important to the birds. Parent condors that Koford observed coming to the nest would perch nearby before entering. This he called the "waiting interval." Sometimes this procedure included a movement from one perch to another, with considerable looking about before finally going to the nest. This perching and watching prior to entering the nest is evidently a natural habit that tends to prevent discovery of the nest by predators, including man. A great many other species practice similar caution and secrecy in going to the nest or den.

Perches near the nest are also used by the young condors during the two-month period in which they are unable to fly after first leaving the nest. Without such places to perch, fledgling condors could easily be caught by predatory mammals.

Koford noted that by the time one fledgling had been out of the nest for two and a half months, it had traveled one mile in several short trips of increasing length. Elevated perches probably aid the fledglings in learning to fly. In December, when one young condor was over seven months old, it was still unable to fly more than about a hundred yards, and was still perching at times in the close vicinity of its nest. Koford saw a young condor that he had banded as a nestling soar a distance of one mile when it was eleven months old. Probably no other bird is so dependent for so long a time on the protective attributes of its nesting territory.

Any bird the size of a young condor just out of the nest, with no more ability to run or fly, would be highly vulnerable to the attack of various predators, such as coyotes, bobcats, and mountain lions, that inhabit the mountains of the condor range. Effective nesting territory would, therefore, require special features offering security and means of escape. In particular, it would need to offer protection against human beings. For as far back as *Gymnogyps californianus* has been known to exist, Man has been a predator of the condor. For this reason, remoteness and seclusion from human activity are first prerequisites of a suitable condor nesting site.

Probably the most useful information to come out of Koford's research was his discovery of the subtle and complex response of nesting condors to human disturbance. His penetrating observations, which were confirmed in the final evidence of broken eggs and dead young, seem to leave no doubt as to the accuracy of his conclusions. In detail he studied certain aspects of the bird's behavior that have been construed by various other observers as indicating tameness and fearlessness toward human beings. As other observers have noted, nesting condors sometimes appear more confused and perplexed than frightened when people invade their nests. Some birds have remained in the nest when a human entered. One such situation was graphically recorded by William L. Finlay in an article in *The Condor* in 1906. In that historic case the parent condor stayed in the nest while a human intruder handled the small nestling within a few feet of the old bird.

Observing behavior of this kind, and subsequent developments, it was Koford's judgment that persons unacquainted with bird psychology often misinterpret the condor's reactions. Behavior at nests that may appear to reflect tameness and lack of fear is actually an innate response to extreme alarm. In this state of alarm certain essential activities, such as feeding the young, are not performed. Twice Koford saw adult condors, which had just been disturbed at a nest, regurgitate chunks of food they had eaten. An adult captured in a nest by some photographers disgorged about a pint of food. At one nest that was closely watched, the egg remained unattended all night after the incubating adult was flushed from the cave the evening before.

Koford found the Sespe area to be the condors' main nesting center and general winter refuge. As a result of his study the Sespe Condor Sanctuary was established. Roughly a rectangle, 12 miles from east to west and 7 miles from north to south, this refuge comprises some 53,000 acres of wild, mountainous terrain with a complex assortment of rock precipices, boulder-strewn slopes, and steep-walled canyons. The condors have used the area since earliest history as a favorite nesting territory. Located near the southeast border of Ventura County in Los Padres National Forest, this odd remnant of wilderness lies, paradoxically, within a few miles of burgeoning, sprawling Los Angeles.

Chapter II

THE OUTLOOK

IN 1963, WITH MY BROTHER EBEN, I WAS ENGAGED by the National Audubon Society to reappraise the status of the condor to determine what changes might have occurred since Koford's findings of the 1940's. This fieldwork was financed by the National Geographic Society.

Early one morning in 1964, when we were well along in our survey, I drove to the Sespe Condor Sanctuary on a public road, or corridor, that extends into a central part of that area. Leaving my light pickup truck near the end of this road, I hiked on past the boundary signs into the closed territory. I had with me the special permit required of all persons entering the refuge.

Passing the buildings of a cattle operation, I took a dim roadway that led for some three miles to one of the higher peaks in the sanctuary. This old mark had been scraped out by a bulldozer a few years before as an access route for vehicles used in the control of forest fire. Its construction inside the closed area had been questioned and it was not to be used except in the event of fire. Following a steep ridge, it passed for most of its distance through an impenetrable sea of chaparral, a dense brushland growth, in some places twelve feet high, that covers most of the Sespe Sanctuary. The condor may owe its survival to this chaparral barrier that makes many of its traditional nesting and roosting places almost inaccessible to man.

On coarse mountainous soils too weak to sustain a grass cover, California's long, dry, almost rainless summers have worked with fire and time to produce the chaparral, a growth distinguished by its capacity to thrive on weak soil, to withstand drought, and to recover quickly from the forest fires that for centuries have swept over these California ranges. A variety of shrub species make up the chaparral, with a half-dozen or more often growing together. The scrub oak, a common member of this association, was known by the Spanish settlers as *chaparro* and from that early name the term "chaparral" has been applied to the whole brushland growth. Although different forest species, including large trees, commonly intermingle with the chaparral, it is this mantle of dense brush cover that mainly clothes the coastal mountains of central and southern California. Except for the one nest in the cavity of the big tree in the mountains east of the San Joaquin Valley, all known condor nests have been found in these chaparral-covered coastal mountains.

Following the bulldozed passageway as it climbed steeply toward the peak, I was pleased to find no recent evidence of human beings after I left the cattle headquarters. This was important, as, on a trip to the peak a few months before, I had discovered an illegal photography project in operation. A four-wheel-drive vehicle had trespassed by traveling up the old fire road and stopping near a condor's nest. The only remaining evidence of that violation was a cardboard flashbulb container that I found under a big spruce where condors commonly roosted.

I noticed the tracks of a black bear that had recently used the same route. The black bear is a newcomer in this southern range of the condor. Sidney Peyton, a pioneer naturalist of Ventura County, had seen no black bears in this region prior to about 1940, but now they are common. The killing off of the grizzlies that formerly inhabited the range, and perhaps made it untenable for the smaller species, may explain this recent bear invasion. One of the last records of a living grizzly in California was of one trapped and shot in a vineyard in lower Tehunga Canyon near Los Angeles in 1922.

Near the top of the high peak, I passed through the grass opening where eighteen years before Carl Koford had watched the lion stalking the deer. Although I had often noticed lion tracks in the sanctuary, I saw no sign of the big cats on this morning's walk. There were four deer in sight where Koford had noted as many as sixty in the 1940's. Several cattle were also grazing on the ripening annual growth on this high *potrero,* or pasture. They were some of the herd let out to graze on this part of the condor refuge through a leasing arrangement between the National Forest and a local private interest. The cattle and deer at this time in late spring were in good condition.

The tracks of a bear or a lion or a human being may bear importantly on condor survival. So may the density and height of the chaparral, or the number and condition of deer or cattle on a particular piece of rangeland. These signs and clues must be seen and understood if there is to be a sound program of condor preservation, and if the full values of such preservation are to be realized.

The old fire road ended short of the high peak. From this point I followed an older, steeper foot trail, overgrown in places by the brush, to reach the summit. This high vantage point, towering above its surroundings at an elevation of over 5,000 feet, overlooks a main section of the Sespe Refuge. In view from here were the territories of a number of condor nests found by Koford in his study of the 1940's.

I had climbed to this high observation point to watch for paired or single adult condors that might indicate an occupied nest. Perhaps parent birds would be bringing food to a nestling. I could thus watch for evidence of reproduction without disturbing the condors. At this time of year, the non-nesting birds that normally compose about two-thirds of the condor population generally leave the refuge and move northward in their foraging and roosting activities—some of the birds traveling as far as 200 miles toward the north—leaving the sanctuary to the nesting pairs and their young.

To the westward, on this bright May morning, I could see a

stretch of the open Pacific near the city of Ventura thirty miles away. To the east about fifteen miles, appearing antlike through my binoculars, a procession of traffic on State Highway 99 hurried northward and southward through the arid mountains between Los Angeles and Bakersfield. Closer, and higher even than my observation point, Cobblestone Mountain rose just beyond the northeast boundary of the condor refuge. From that point westward a ridge of other rugged peaks that tower above the steep north wall of Sespe Canyon shut off my view to the northwest.

By midafternoon, after some six hours of watching, I had seen no condors. However, I had seen golden eagles, turkey vultures, and the various species of hawks commonly observed in the condor range, which, at a distance, may be mistaken for condors. At different times I identified a pair of red-tailed hawks circling over a point some two miles distant. At about noon a turkey vulture passed high over the peak in the tilting glide that characterizes that species. A covey of California quail, all adults, fed along the edge of the grassland opening below me, then moved back out of sight in the chaparral.

It was significant that no young birds were in this covey. Usually at this season the quail are in isolated pairs, nesting or rearing broods. In drought years, however, the annual nesting activities are shortened. The pairs regroup early in these seasons, and fewer young are reared than when rainfall is near to or above average. Although late rains had produced a normal spring growth at this higher elevation, extreme drought had prevailed through most of the region. Accordingly, the quail, even these in a local area of normal spring growth, had prematurely terminated their annual nesting efforts.

The prolific and sedentary quail are evidently endowed with some natural mechanism through which reproduction is deferred in seasons of possible food shortage. Excessive numbers that might jeopardize the entire population are thus avoided. As I watched this covey of quail move about in its busy foraging, I thought of their subtle and unexplained system of population control, and my attention wandered off toward the south and toward other aspects of population and survival. Almost within sight in that direction was a human population that in its continued, unabated growth offered a dramatic contrast to the regulated numbers of the quail.

When I first arrived at my high lookout that morning, the air had been clear for several miles around. South of the condor refuge, toward the town of Fillmore, I could see the level floor of the Santa Clara Valley covered with citrus groves. That fertile lowland still kept much of its rural aspect. Just beyond the Santa Clara Valley I could see the oil derricks on Oak Ridge. Condors have been known to cross the valley to forage along Oak Ridge and the north side of the Simi Valley. This area, much of which was still open stock range, was rapidly turning into another area of high-density housing in the northward spread of Los Angeles.

Beyond Oak Ridge this morning a rising, spreading mass of murky air had marked the general location of Los Angeles. The smog had steadily moved closer during the day. By late afternoon it had spread over the Santa Clara Valley and was filling the canyons of the condor refuge to a height of around three thousand feet. Now, looking in the direction of Fillmore, I could barely make out landmarks five miles away. Similar landmarks ten miles away had been clearly visible in the morning.

As I looked out upon this spreading blanket of foul air, I thought again of survival. What about the effects on the condors of this new, man-made factor in their environment? To what extent would the change in visibility affect their success in foraging? What of the direct physical effects? I had recently read an agricultural report of smog damage to agricultural crops in over twenty counties of California. I had seen native trees that were dying from the effects of polluted air. I had experienced the eye irritation that attacks one in smog of high density. What was the effect of this on the telescopic eye of the condor?

In speculating on these questions from my high lookout, up where the air was still clear and I was the only human being for miles around, I wondered which would finally outlast the smog, the condor or man. Which of the two species was most endangered by this man-made threat? Or was the survival of both equally involved? Could the two species be fellow travelers on the ever-challenging, ever-testing road of survival—one threatened by its own too little, the other by its own too much? At this point of my speculation, something startled the covey of quail that had again moved out into the grass opening. The roar of their wings as they took the chaparral brought my attention back to condor watching.

From my high observation point, I occasionally skimmed the

skyline with my binoculars; for condors are most commonly sighted on the wing against the sky, and generally not far above the horizon. To examine distant objects, I had with me a twenty-power telescope. A red-tailed hawk, evidently one of the pair I had seen in the morning, was again circling over the same point. Otherwise I could find nothing in sight that called for more than a casual look. A few white-throated swifts were cutting arcs in the air over a nearby cliff, and a small flock of band-tailed pigeons flew across a canyon below.

Off toward the northeast I now gave special attention to the skyline. On another day I had watched condors as they spiraled upward from a particular canyon in this area in the morning to gain altitude and at last line out in their incredible glide toward their traditional foraging grounds twenty miles or more to the north. In late afternoon of the same day I had seen condors return to the same canyon.

It was late afternoon. My view through the binoculars came randomly to rest on Whitaker Peak, which stood about eight miles toward the northeast, across Piru Canyon from the condor refuge. On a lookout tower on the prominent peak a fire watch was kept by the Forest Service during the dry season. As I scrutinized the distant watchtower, I noted what first appeared as a speck of dust on the lenses of the binoculars. But the speck was moving, and it moved in a way that only one kind of speck could move across the field of a pair of binoculars.

The glide of a condor is different from any other movement in nature. Except at times in gaining altitude or maneuvering about in landing and taking off, the condor soars with only occasional flapping or dipping of the wings. As it cruises along in a steady, effortless glide, the big bird seems suspended from above rather than supported from below. The great wings are not completely outstretched but are somewhat flexed, curving slightly forward from the body to about halfway out, then bending slightly backward to the tip. Of the long, finger-like pinions at the wing tips, the ones ahead bend upward on the passing air, while those behind droop slightly downward. It may be this strange droop of the back feathers of the wing tips that makes soaring condors appear to be hanging without exertion in the air.

The speck in the glass grew larger as it moved, obviously coming my way. And although it quickly grew to be a big bird, and its steady flight was already a first indication that it was a condor, it was still too far away to identify with certainty even with the telescope. But I didn't have long to wait. The soaring bird came on, high over the lower Aqua Blanca Canyon and moving closer toward the northeast corner of the condor refuge. When about two miles away, in a sudden dip of the wings the long, level glide changed to a downward slant toward the canyon where I had previously seen condors leave and return. Quickly it was below the skyline, skimming low along a chaparral slope, and appearing to feel its way through the changing air currents along the canyon wall. Here I noted the occasional downward flexing of the wrists and hand-like fingerings of first one wing tip, then the other. All these are idiosyncrasies unique to the condor. Finally, as it turned my way and banked, I saw the white patches under the wings that are used most commonly to identify condors. And at last, when it was about a mile away, and just before it dropped out of sight into the canyon, I identified through the binoculars the bare, yellowish-orange skin of the head and neck that showed this bird to be an adult condor at least six years old.

Looking around a while longer for further signs of condors, and making another sweep of the skyline, I put down a few last notes. Then I took a final look out toward the northeast where the condor had first appeared. In the distance, about fifteen miles away, I could see Liebre Mountain where another lookout tower was located. Beyond that, another eight miles to the northward, the western ridge of the Tehachapi Mountains topped the horizon. There, on the broad southeast rim of the San Joaquin Valley, the big Tejon Ranch sprawls over some 292,000 acres. Most of the big ranch is rangeland well stocked with cattle and in some portions sheep. It is also the range of an extensive deer herd. It could well be that as many deer were ranging the Tejon at the time of my observation as at any time in its history—as many or more, perhaps, than over a century before, when a Hungarian naturalist, János Xántus, exploring this part of California in 1857, noted grizzly bears in abundance around Fort Tejon. Some of those grizzlies he mentioned as being extremely ferocious, driving him twice to climb to safety in trees.

Actually, these far rangelands were closely involved with the functioning of the Sespe Condor Sanctuary, especially if the bird I had just seen was returning to a nest. The survival of condors, and all other species, depends first on an adequate food supply. And of the general supply, that which is available to nesting birds, and therefore provides for successful reproduction, is usually crucial. In the survey I was working on, I was giving particular attention to the question of available food for nesting condors. As yet, after more than a year of investigation, I had found no evidence that food was lacking. In fact, all indications had consistently pointed to an ample, sustained supply of carrion.

However, a food scarcity that might limit condor reproduction could easily escape detection in a year and a half of the most careful field investigation. How far, I wondered, could a pair of condors range from a central nesting site to find food for themselves and return with food for a nestling? How would the present supply and availability of condor food on the Tejon compare with what it was when grizzlies chased the exploring naturalist into the trees there a little over a century ago? How would the food be distributed as to time and place? For it would be the minimum supply, available during any period of any season, year, or decade, that would be the crucial supply. Any serious food shortage would cause a failure of reproduction. Nesting condors, either tending to the duties of incubation or rearing of young, would require a stable supply of available food to a greater degree than non-nesting members of the population. Successful reproduction would therefore confirm an adequate supply of available condor food, at least for the period in which any nestling condor was reared. I was thinking of these and other aspects of condor food as I took this last look northward toward the far ridges of the Tehachapis.

Evening shadows were stretching across the canyons as I finally left the peak and headed back toward the public road. Coming back into the grassland opening where Koford had watched the lion stalk the deer, I flushed the covey of quail that was again foraging along the edge.

The sun was setting as I came in view of my parked truck. From there I drove on a short distance and camped for the night at a public campground where the road ends in the condor refuge. In the morning I would take a trip northward, for over a hundred miles, to my ranch in the Red Hills of eastern San Luis Obispo County near the little town of Shandon where I was born and raised.

Chapter III

THE EGG COLLECTORS

IN THE EARLY 1880's MY GRANDPARENTS HAD come from eastern Canada with seven grown sons and daughters, all to take up adjoining homesteads in a canyon of the open rolling hill country near Shandon. After the sons married and their children reached school age, all but one of the family moved to more settled areas near the coast. My father, although he was also the head of a young, growing family of five boys and two girls, remained on his homestead wheat-and-cattle ranch in McMillan Canyon, a leader in the new and growing pioneer community.

When the Southern Pacific Railroad first reached from the north into the upper Salinas Valley in the late 1880's, it brought a wheat boom to the rich, rolling grasslands around Shandon, a pioneering epic that, in many respects, was fully as romantic as the California

Gold Rush, the era of the big ranchos, or the lumbering booms of the early West.

The country was big and new, and quickly the ingenious settlers developed and adopted big new methods of farming. Great teams of horses and mules pulled and powered big implements and big freight wagons. My father's combine harvester, owned and operated in partnership with a neighbor, was pulled over the steeply rolling wheatfields by a team of thirty-three horses. When harvested, the wheat, packaged in large burlap sacks, was hauled to the railroad, twenty miles away, in freight wagons drawn by ten-horse teams. These long-line teams were guided and controlled by the use of a single "jerk line" fastened to the bridle of a lead horse. The loads of grain would equal a ton for each horse in the team.

To a person not acquainted with such an operation, the sight of a combine harvester that, with a twenty-foot swath, cut, gathered, threshed, and separated the standing grain, would seem incredible. Four or five men formed the crew. From the front of the machine a sloping ladder extended upward and outward over the herdlike mass of horses. At the end of this ladder was a seat from which the driver controlled the big team. To do so, he used two lines of light ropes that reached out to the far lead horses. At his side was a big whip—a long, tapering rod with a longer lash of braided rawhide fastened to the tip. At his feet was a box of fair-sized rocks. In guiding and controlling the course and speed of the great team, there was skillful use of the two lines, as well as a wide assortment of shouts, an occasional cracking of the big whip, which sounded much like shots from a pistol, and for some lagging horse an accurately thrown rock. These were the showman-like techniques of the driver in the high, swaying seat.

Like a roaring, grinding juggernaut the big harvester was drawn round the fields of standing wheat, around and over the steeply sloping hills. Sometimes, on the sharp crest of a hill, the forward part of the big team would be out of the driver's sight. To a boy too young yet for such glory and adventure, the spectacle was one of wonder, excitement, and of highest aspiration.

After the harvest, with the grain being freighted to the railroad, a day's journey away, the drivers of the long-line teams on the wheat wagons became the heroes. Some had specially made bells that fitted on the harness of the lead span. Swinging along a deeply rutted road on a hot day in late summer, with horses, wagons, and driver all but hidden from sight in a cloud of rising dust, the spirit of the whole pioneer movement was dramatically echoed in the sound of these team bells. Over the toil and hardship, gaiety and a zest for the rough, free life prevailed.

Even greater heroes than the harvest hands and long-line teamsters were the *vaqueros,* or buckaroos, that tended the cattle of the big ranchos. The road that followed McMillan Canyon was used as a cattle trail by several large ranches in moving herds to market. With other younger members of our family I recall watching these herds go by. Several hundred grown steers would be herded and driven by a dozen or so men on horseback. Except when they were branded and marked as calves, the cattle on the big ranches of that day often reached full growth with no other acquaintance with human beings. Some were semiwild. The horses ridden by the buckaroos were generally of the bronco or mustang type and, like the cattle, also tended to be wild and skittish.

In keeping with a tradition that evidently developed and grew out of necessity in the settlement of the Wild West, a studied recklessness and disdain toward danger characterized the demeanor of these ranch hands. Like the cattle they herded and the horses they rode, some of them appeared to be half wild also. This general appearance of being free and undomesticated was further accentuated by the regalia they wore. The cultural traits of the native Indian, the artistically inclined Spanish, and the ingenious frontiersman from east across the mountains were blended in the garb and working paraphernalia of these picturesque horsemen. Each sombrero, neckerchief, or jangling pair of spurs, although conforming to a general atmosphere of jaunty adventure, was different according to the individuality of the wearer. As we watched the exciting cavalcades pass along the winding canyon road, these whooping, whistling, galloping riders with their skittish mounts and their colorful, picturesque trappings left indelible impressions on our young minds. To become a wild buckaroo became even more of a boyish ambition than success as a competent harvest hand or long-line teamster.

But as I grew into my teens, the local adventurer who interested me most was Kelly Truesdale, the egg collector. Kelly, raised in the

2. *(Above)* A 29-day-old condor chick. 3. *(Below)* An 82-day-old condor chick.

4. *(Above)* The raised back feathers of this 112-day-old condor chick show its alarm. 5. *(Below)* This juvenile condor, 175 days old, has left the nest but as yet can only fly short distances.

6. Pair of adult condors with young, photographed in 1906.

Shandon community, was a small boy when the town was first established in the late 1880's. During the time when he was growing up, the little settlement typified the smaller outposts throughout the western frontier of that period. A post office, schoolhouse, church, general store, blacksmith shop, and a two-story hotel with bar were its main establishments. Inhabited by no more than about fifty people, it was the hub of the farming boom that had begun with the coming of the homesteaders. Although various big ranchos that were established during the earlier grazing boom still covered great portions of the region, an almost equal area soon became marked by the barbed-wire fences and farming operations of the homesteaders.

Strangely, however, although farming and livestock grazing were the principal occupations, the settlers of the new territory were not mainly of farming or ranching background. The land rush in California, following, as it did, the Gold Rush, was not a movement primarily of agricultural people. In a social gathering of the Shandon community around 1900, with people coming from miles around, the backgrounds represented would be extremely varied. In one canyon a doctor, a schoolteacher, a carpenter, a musician, and a former barkeeper occupied neighboring homesteads. The Spanish and Indian vaqueros, picturesque but competent, were predominant among the workers of the big ranchos. Also in a usual community gathering would be a few of the drifters and adventurers who, probably as much as any other type, represented the men of the western frontier.

The problem of bare subsistence was common among the settlers, many of whom had large families. Wild game was an important source of food for many homestead tables. There was some commercial hunting, and trapping of furbearing species was common. With this dependence on game and other wildlife, marksmanship and other hunting skills were important. Prowess with a gun was a mark of high distinction among the pioneers of the Shandon community, as it was throughout the entire West at that time. This glorification of the hunt and the kill, without consideration for the game supply, worked with economic stress to mold a general philosophy of resource use. In this philosophy there was no concern for destruction or depletion. The wealth of the new land was there for the taking. It was a philosophy of plunder, of conquest, and of maximum, immediate exploitation.

During this period there were practically no effective laws operating in eastern San Luis Obispo County to inhibit the killing of any form of wildlife. And although the game resource was already dwindling, and in some sections was completely wiped out, hunting continued with undiminished eagerness. The killing of a few last antelope at different points in the surrounding region, the last survivors of a few remnant herds, were exploits that would remain in local history as memorable achievements.

Wildlife of whatever species was commonly shot on sight. The more uncommon or rare the target, the more quick and eager was the shooting. The philosophy of conservation and of wildlife preservation, then in its infancy anywhere in the West, had not yet reached Shandon. Reared and schooled in the customs, traditions, and hunting philosophy of this frontier community, Kelly Truesdale became noted for another form of exploiting the new wildlife resource. He became a professional collector of bird eggs.

Kelly started out on his collecting expeditions early each spring. First on horseback or in a horse-drawn cart, and later in a small car of an early model, he would arrive at the ranch in McMillan Canyon. Smelling of sagebrush and chewing a quid of tobacco, with a reddish beard that always seemed to be of about midgrowth, he was fully as colorful and intriguing a figure as any of the buckaroos or teamsters, with exciting adventures in store: A pair of golden eagles had nested in some tall pine that Kelly was reluctant to climb alone. He could not reach a falcon's nest in some overhanging cliff without help. First, one of my older brothers would join in these adventures. But soon I too was old enough to accompany Kelly in his collecting exploits.

The hunting of bird eggs required more insight into natural history than ranching activities in which physical skill and strength were the main requirements. In addition, Kelly emphasized the scientific and philosophical aspects of his collecting. We were gathering and recording scientific facts. Although the economic return made the collecting feasible, the pursuit of accurate knowledge was a main purpose. The eggs and accompanying data we collected were contributions to the growing science of ornithology. This work for something not of immediate practical need or use was profoundly different from the ranching activities in which economic gain was the driving purpose.

1458236
Traveling the back ranges and valleys of the big ranches, visiting the cliffs where ravens and prairie falcons nested, searching the woodlands of pine and oak for the high nests of golden eagles, we continually learned about the local bird life and its nesting habits. We were studying the principles and the workings of ecology long before the new science was heard of in the condor country.

Camping at night in the cottonwoods along a remote creek bottom, we would listen to the wild howling and yapping of the coyotes. Even more, we heard the great horned owls, using old nests in the cottonwoods that were built in previous years by red-tailed hawks. The vocal repertoire of these big owls, as revealed in the nightly conversation of a nesting pair, would often be the subject of our campfire discussions. With these night sounds to accent his words, by the warmth and light of a cottonwood fire, Kelly would tell me of his collecting adventures. Those that involved the condor were always fascinating to me, and the most fascinating of all was Kelly's story of how he discovered his first condor nest.

It began on a hot afternoon in June, about 1907. With the bird-nesting season over, Kelly was working as a ranch hand on the Carrisa Plains some thirty miles southeast of Shandon. The plains are a high level stretch of open country, bordered on each side by rugged mountains. Kelly was pitching hay that lay in long wind-rows across one of the few patches of cropland on the Carrisa at that time. As he toiled in the hot sun, a large shadow passed swiftly across the hayfield within a few feet of him. Startled by this movement, and looking up, he saw his first condor.

From what he had heard and read of condors, there was no doubt in Kelly's mind about the identification of the big bird. The great size; the dark plumage with long, triangular white patches that tapered outward under the forepart of the wings; the bare, yellowish-orange skin of the head and neck; the steady, majestic glide; and, as he stood quietly watching, a barely audible, buzzing whistle as warm, rising air over the open plain passed through and under the bending pinions—all were identification marks of the condor that had been well impressed on the mind of the young collector.

As in a trance Kelly watched the gliding figure become a spot in the distance and at last fade from sight in the direction of a dark canyon in the mountains west of the Carrisa. Even after the big bird had disappeared, Kelly's eyes remained fixed on the far canyon.

Condor eggs were then bringing 250 dollars or more each. To earn as much pitching hay, he would have to work from daylight till dark for 250 days.

The following February, about the time that condors would be nesting, Kelly, with a trusted companion, worked his way through a wilderness of chaparral near the foot of the mountain range where the condor had disappeared the summer before. Taking turns with an ax, the two bearded youths worked eagerly as they cut a trail through the tall, dense brush. As one chopped, the other led a pack mule loaded with camping equipment and supplies. On top of the pack, firmly tied in place, was a long telescope.

After a day of chopping brush and coaxing the mule across dangerous places in the steep terrain, they finally pitched camp on the peak of a low hill in the midst of the chaparral. On the rugged mountain slope upward from this lookout was a steep canyon overhung by a towering, precipitous wall of broken rock. It was the same wild canyon Kelly had seen the summer before when he watched the condor sail out of sight across the Carrisa.

Traces of snow from a recent winter storm remained on shaded parts of the rock bluff. Considerably more rain and snow fall at these elevations than on the lower open country to the east. Even on the Temblor Range, of equal elevation but lying some twenty miles away on the east side of the Carrisa Plains, the climate was much more arid. These widely contrasting conditions of climate and terrain, all within an hour's flight of a condor, provided a wide ecological diversity. Probably more than any single feature, this panoramic variety marked the general region as condor country.

It was late evening as Kelly and his confederate finally completed the clearing and arranging of their camp. The pack mule was tethered some distance away in a small, grassy opening. A pail of water was carried up from the bottom of the wild canyon where a small stream of clear water was running. To keep their presence in the area as inconspicuous as possible, they would build no campfire. After a cold meal, and with blankets spread on the bare ground, the two youths, exhausted from a day of chopping their way through the chaparral, were ready for sleep. Taking a last look around in the quiet dusk, they could still see, on the eastern horizon beyond the Carrisa, the faint outline of the Temblor Range. Much nearer, somewhere along the edge of the chaparral, a coyote howled, and nearer than that, in one of the canyon bottoms a screech owl whistled its sequence of low soft notes. But as the two youths looked and listened for a last few moments, in the direction of the wild canyon and its towering rock wall there were only darkness and silence.

By sunrise the next morning, after another fireless meal and while his partner changed the tether of the pack mule, Kelly Truesdale scanned the rock wall through the telescope. Passing back and forth, he gradually concentrated on a particular shelf under a high over-hanging ledge. Extending downward just below the shelf were white markings that Kelly recognized as the excrement of roosting birds. Sheltered by the overhanging ledge, the shelf would be a likely place for condors to roost.

Although Truesdale was seeing this area for the first time, there was something about it that seemed familiar. A year or two previously he had been told by a professional condor hunter of a place somewhere in this same mountain range where condors had once roosted and been systematically hunted for their skins. The area he was now watching resembled in detail the description of that historic roosting place, especially as it included a grove of tall pines that grew just above the crest of the rocky bluff where the slope of the mountain became more gradual.

From the story Kelly had heard, which was supported by other accounts and records, a number of the birds used this place as a favorite roosting site. Some occasionally perched at night on the shelf of protected rock, but in milder weather nearly all the group roosted in the pines just above. The strategy used by this hunter had become a local legend.

Except for the birds that are nesting, condors commonly gather into groups in foraging and in roosting. But in leaving and return-ing to the roosts, the birds follow one another at some distance rather than in close group formation as do most species of flocking birds. When together on the roosts, and often at feeding sites, condors will usually leave one at a time, sometimes at intervals of several minutes.

Knowing this behavior and the aversion of condors to gunfire, the hunter would hide at night within shooting range of the roost. The next morning, as the condors, one after another, left their perches, he would wait until all but the last one had left. This lone bird could then be shot without alarming the others. The others might return again in the evening, permitting another kill on successive mornings, repeated as long as any condors returned to the roost.

As Kelly studied the high promontory and speculated on its possible history, a twinge of apprehension mingled with his thoughts. What chance would there be that even a lone pair of the rare birds had escaped that systematic hunting project? For decades, as Truesdale knew, condor hunting had been a profitable business. Since the gun first came within range of a condor, the big birds had been shot by hunters of all types, some as trophies, or for other purposes of display. Some were taken as scientific specimens. Others were shot as mere targets or out of nothing more than curiosity to "see what they looked like." The lone condor Truesdale had watched passing over the Carrisa the summer before was the only one he had ever seen while searching for bird eggs. Possibly this was the last condor in all eastern San Luis Obispo County.

The sun was almost an hour high when Kelly's friend returned from changing the tether of the pack mule. It was bright on the more exposed parts of the great bluff, and at about a mile away the shelf under the high ledge now showed more distinctly through the telescope. Two large birds suddenly appeared, circling above the point, and brought the two watchers to quick attention. But from their dark plumage and lighter build, they were quickly recognized as adult golden eagles.

Of the various sounds that came from the chaparral on this bright, late winter morning, the piping song of the little wren tit was most common, a sequence of high notes increasing in tempo toward the end. There was the melody of the California thrasher, a relative of the mockingbird, and the high, melancholy note of the mountain quail. Occasionally in the bottom of a canyon a California jay gave its rasping screech, and once from somewhere in the area of the cliffs, Kelly thought he heard the wailing cry of a falcon. It would have been a peregrine or the more common prairie falcon, either of which might be preparing to nest in one of the more precipitous cliffs.

As the morning sun threw added light on the protected shelf under the high ledge, something focused the attention of the two watchers. Taking turns with the telescope, they studied a dark form, barely distinct against the shaded recess in the cliff. Once they were quite sure the object had changed its position, moving outward toward the edge of the shelf. Almost immediately after this it moved again. What was now obviously a big bird spread its wings and launched itself from the shelf. It glided for a short distance and lit on a high boulder on the point of the bluff. During this short flight the two youths could plainly see the bright patches of white under the big bird's wings. It was a condor. Kelly was trembling as he handed the telescope to his partner. All they needed now was another condor, to make a nesting pair.

After resting on the boulder for several minutes, the condor again spread its wings. But this time instead of taking flight it remained perched with its great pinions extended. For a few minutes the big bird remained in this "sunning" position that is characteristic of condors and turkey vultures. Its purpose is evidently to dry the flight feathers of dampness that may have gathered during the night. Standing on the high boulder with its expansive wings extended to each side and held perpendicular to the morning sun, to the two young egg collectors the great bird appeared as an apparition from some other world.

While his friend, who now had the telescope, studied the first condor he had ever seen, a movement lower in the canyon caught Truesdale's eye. It was another big bird circling upward, and as it turned and banked it also showed the long, bright triangles of white under the wings. Two condors were in the territory. They could be a nesting pair.

After several circles this second condor soared outward from the cliffs in an unwavering glide toward the Carrisa. As it passed from sight, the two watchers turned their attention back to the first bird, which somewhat to their surprise was still perched quietly on the high boulder. If these birds were a mated pair, why had they not been together? Why did the one remain while the other flew out toward the distant foraging grounds?

As the young collectors were discovering, a pair of nesting condors take turns at incubating the egg and brooding the nestling. They generally relieve each other at the nest in ways that will least disclose its location. This secrecy, evidently innate, has probably worked to prevent predators, including man, from finding the nests.

After several minutes of standing motionless on the boulder, the condor, with a few strokes of its wings followed by an easy glide, also headed out toward the Carrisa. But after a short flight in that direction it circled and came back, soaring low along the face of the rock wall. Passing on toward the head of the wild canyon, it circled again and landed on a ledge. From there it seemed to look about intently for a few minutes, after which it dropped from the ledge in lowering flight and disappeared among the jutting boulders.

For several minutes the two young egg men, almost breathless from excitement, watched for the condor to reappear. The place where it had disappeared was the most rugged part of the towering rock wall. It was near the area where the other condor had first appeared. Could it be that the other bird had left a nest while its mate, now out of sight in the cliff, was taking its turn at incubating an egg? As the minutes passed, it became obvious that the condor was staying in the rocks.

It would require several hours of chopping brush and negotiating the steeper portions of the rock wall to reach the spot where the condor had gone. But the two confederates were soon eagerly at work, one taking his turn with the ax while the other carried a length of rope and a two-pound coffee can filled with cotton. Hours later, as the shadows of late afternoon began to darken the canyon, they reached the foot of the cliff and began to work their way upward. Most of the rock slope was too steep to climb without a rope. Perpendicular in places, it included overhanging ledges from which a fall would have meant sure death. Finding a route where there were crevices to follow and bushes to cling to, the two climbers were finally able to reach a central point in the great bluff.

From here, as he scanned the rugged area just above, Kelly's attention settled on the steep face of a massive boulder. Midway in this huge rock which jutted out from the main bluff there was a hole about a foot and a half in diameter. At one side of this opening something odd-looking and brightly colored had caught his eye. Truesdale quickly pointed this out to his friend, and together they scrutinized the strange object. Light orange in color, it was the head of a condor. The great bird was quietly peering at them from the entrance of the small cave. They were no more than fifty feet away, and they could now make out the beak, the red iris of the eye, a small cap of black feathers across the crown just above the eyes, and a ruff, or collar, of bristle-like feathers midway on the neck below the bare reddish skin.

Not sure what to do next, Kelly gave a piercing yell. His partner clapped his hands. At this, all doubt about the identity of the strange object was quickly settled. Scrambling through the hole, the condor flapped heavily outward over their heads. Then to their continued amazement it turned back and landed no more than a hundred feet away on a point of the cliff. Standing there peering about, first in one direction then another, the great bird appeared more perplexed and confused than afraid.

Oddly, in this last wild hideout, this condor seemed to have no great fear of human beings. This strange behavior that now perplexed the two young egg collectors would eventually become a main cause of misconception and disagreement in matters of condor preservation.

Tense with eagerness and anticipation, the two climbers worked their way around the side and to the top of the huge boulder, where they found a small foothold. From here, with his partner holding the rope, and with the two-pound coffee can buttoned inside the front of his shirt, Kelly lowered himself to the mouth of the cave. Then, as he looked upward to his companion, his high-pitched yell again echoed across the wild canyon. It was the yell of a triumphant egg collector.

From an entrance barely large enough for a slim man to squeeze through, the cave immediately broadened into a space some 10 feet long, 6 feet wide, and 3 feet in height. Near the back wall on the sandy floor was a large white egg almost 5 inches in length. It was larger than any egg Kelly had ever collected.

Kelly removed the coffee can from the front of his shirt, pulled off the tight lid, and took out the padded cotton. Quickly and carefully he wrapped the big egg in the soft material and fitted it snugly in the can. With the package again buttoned safely inside his shirt, and with his partner pulling on the rope, he climbed back to the top of the big boulder.

After a last look at the condor which still perched above them on the point, the two tired youths hurried back down the trail they had chopped through the chaparral. It was almost dark by the time they reached their camp. With no further need for stealth, they could have a blazing campfire and their first hot meal since early the day before.

After supper, by the warming glow of the fire, they planned the next day. At dawn they would start homeward, toward the north, on a trip of some thirty miles through the open ranchlands to Shandon, the little frontier settlement where they had been raised. They again heard the howling of a coyote, off toward the east where the chaparral changed to grassland. Nearby a screech owl gave its muted whistle. But as the campfire died and the two youths moved toward their blankets, it was not the next day's events or the sounds of the mountain night that held their deeper thoughts; neither was it the big egg in the two-pound coffee can. In the mind of each as they gazed through the darkness toward the wild canyon was the somber, brooding figure of a giant bird standing as if perplexed and confused, but strangely unafraid, on the point of a wilderness bluff.

It was as heroes that the two young egg collectors returned from their successful adventure in the mountains. Except for Kelly and his partner, no more than one or two of the local settlers had ever seen a condor, although some had hunted and explored extensively throughout the region. Of the various trophies and specimens of particular interest that had been collected in the surrounding region, the big egg they brought home in the two-pound coffee can was the first of its kind. An account of the event was carried in the county newspaper, published in San Luis Obispo, the county seat, some fifty miles from Shandon. This article referred to the condor egg as having a cash value equal to its weight in gold.

The high bluff where the condor nest had been found, although thirty miles away toward the southeast, could be seen from the Shandon Post Office. Yet, in all his searching of the area for nesting birds, Kelly had never caught sight of a condor until he had taken the hay-pitching job on the Carrisa Plains. Condors were evidently extremely rare in eastern San Luis Obispo County throughout this period of early settlement. In fact, there is considerable evidence that the entire species was close to extinction around 1908 when Kelly took his first condor egg, perhaps closer to extinction than at any time before or after.

After a few days of basking in the local limelight, Kelly prepared the condor egg as a scientific specimen. This required removal of its contents through a small hole in the shell. He then put it up for sale through the same trade channels in which he had sold other, less rare, bird eggs for several years. For at least twenty years prior to 1908, the sale and trade of bird eggs had been a growing practice throughout the entire country and especially in California. The West was still new. The Gold Rush had focused world attention on California. The natural history of the new land was of worldwide interest. At that time, also, the search for new species and specimens of rare or significant wildlife was at a peak. Museums and other scientific and educational institutions, together with certain government agencies, sent out expeditions to gather new material for their displays and collections.

Along with this professional and official collecting, private collecting of the same nature became a fad. Collecting bird eggs was one of the most common specialties. Several of the young men who grew up with Kelly Truesdale in the Shandon community had considerable experience as egg collectors. However, after boyhood this activity was usually dropped for more economically gainful pursuits. But from a youthful amateur Kelly went on to become a renowned professional, selling rare eggs and working as a guide for wealthy collectors making expeditions into the Shandon area.

Oology, the study of bird eggs, was of such common interest in the nineteenth and early twentieth centuries that it supported a widely circulated publication, *The Oologist*. This periodical served mainly to publish information about the sale and exchange of eggs and the activities of various collectors.

When Kelly began to negotiate the sale of his condor egg, the market had been bullish. In 1895, H. R. Taylor, one of the most active dealers, published an offer to pay $250 each for three condor eggs. This trader was presumably selling the eggs at a profit. In 1905, he reported that his hired collectors had taken nine condor eggs, two of which went to a woman collector in the East.

Carl Koford, in his research of the 1940's, found records of nineteen condor eggs being collected in the three-year period 1900–1902. During this period the condor was evidently suffering more from its human associate than at any time since man first entered his range as a wandering aborigine some ten thousand years or more before. This was the heyday of the professional egg collector and the paid hunter. It was the era in which the grizzly bear would pass from the California scene forever. The antelope would disappear from the condor range, and the tule elk would dwindle to a few relict herds. On the national scene the buffalo and passenger pigeon were already close to extinction. The condor, rare to begin with, and suffering every adversity that man could bring against it, would dwindle also. But, amazingly, the great bird would somehow hang on, with survivors finding a few last places of refuge and escape, beyond the reach of man.

Kelly finally made an arrangement to meet a prospective buyer in Paso Robles, the nearest large town that was on the railroad. This prospect was W. Lee Chambers, a salesman of sporting goods, mainly guns and ammunition. An amateur ornithologist and egg collector, Chambers was a leader in the Cooper Ornithological Club. In 1908 he became its business manager, and had a wide acquaintance in the field.

Meeting him at the sporting-goods store in Paso Robles, Kelly produced the big egg for Chambers' appraisal. And here, with the final reward of a year's planning and work almost within his grasp, with the success of an amazing venture about to materialize, disaster struck.

Chambers, an authority on condor eggs, after examining Kelly's egg refused to buy it on the grounds that it appeared to be an egg of some other species. He explained that except for a slight difference in color, the egg of a European swan resembled that of a condor. Some unknown but highly enterprising collector had recently passed off and sold a few swan eggs as condor eggs, and the alarm had been sent out through various channels of the broad oological trade. Lee Chambers had noted that the egg Kelly offered for sale was creamy white, slightly different from the light-greenish tinge of other condor eggs Chambers had handled.

Chambers was adamant. His refusal to buy the big egg was crushing to Truesdale, for Lee Chambers was an active leader in oological circles. His judgment that Truesdale might be trying to sell a bogus egg would have wide influence. Kelly would have to prove that he had found an active condor nest and that the particular birds nesting at that location laid an unusual, cream-colored egg.

In appealing his case among those of his colleagues who he thought might be concerned, Kelly, as a remote possibility, sent an explanation of his predicament to a wealthy collector living in Massachusetts. This was a far place to be casting to for help. Furthermore, the fact that the collector, a Mr. John E. Thayer, already had seven condor eggs in his private collection greatly lessened the possibility that he would be in the market for any more. With surprise and elation Kelly received a reply from Thayer informing him that if satisfactory verification could be established, he would buy the controversial egg at a price of $300. This was more money than Truesdale had expected to receive from Lee Chambers. And here was his opportunity to verify his condor egg and clear his reputation.

For the next two years, in early spring Kelly was back at his former camp in the chaparral, watching the high bluff above the wild canyon. At last a pair of condors were again in the area, and after a few days of observation Kelly was certain that they were nesting. The young oologist hurried back the thirty miles to Shandon and mailed a letter to the eastern collector, saying that the yet unsold condor egg could now be verified.

Thayer's response, though it had to cross the country, was prompt. He asked William Leon Dawson, eminent ornithologist and writer, who then lived in Santa Barbara, about 150 miles south of Shandon, to accompany Kelly back to the condor nest. Dawson at the time was gathering material for his classic work on the birds of California. The trip into the condor country to test the validity of Kelly's controversial condor egg would provide useful information.

On a day in early April a party of three was on its way. Truesdale and Dawson, garbed in the most practical frontier fashion, one bearded, the other with neatly trimmed mustache and goatee, rode in a horse-drawn cart that also carried provisions for the camp, a large camera, and Kelly's two-pound coffee can filled with cotton. Mounted on a second horse, a beardless local youth (my oldest brother) rode at one side. All along the main street as they left the little settlement, they were sent on their way by shouts of goodwill and encouragement.

For a day and a half the strange expedition moved along, passing first through the homesteads that surrounded the little town, then into the open stock ranges, and at last onto the rugged, chaparral slopes of the condor country. Accurately and in detail, Dawson, a gifted and accomplished writer, noted the surrounding landscape, near and far. The California springtime was in full bloom. In the pastures wildflowers of various colors and species mingled with the more typical range grasses. As the rolling rangelands reached the mountains, woodlands of pine and oak took over. Farther on, this changed to the more solid cover of the chaparral.

Seeing this part of California for the first time, Dawson was deeply impressed. As they passed from the big ranches, in size up to 60,000 acres, and on into the wooded back country, it seemed to him that the little party had left civilization behind and entered a fabulous land. Later, Dawson said that the true heart of California lay here in the condor country of eastern San Luis Obispo County.

They camped on the second night in the brush below the big bluff, and made an early start next morning to the condor's nest. In a dramatic account of this final adventure, Dawson described the struggle through the chaparral and the climb up toward the nest cave. He told of three condors, two adults and a darker immature, that circled high above the cliffs, with one of the adults finally lowering into the area of the nest.

As on Truesdale's first trip of discovery, the old condor remained in the cave until the invading party was at the foot of the big rock. As it finally left the nest to perch on a nearby boulder, again there was no pronounced show of alarm or fear. Dawson, studying the great bird as it perched quietly some sixty feet away, later described its attitude as one of gentle dignity. But to Kelly, already a veteran observer of nesting birds, the condor's demeanor was one of perplexity and confusion. To his practiced eye it seemed unable to comprehend what was again happening at the nest it had selected, as far out of human reach as it could find.

With triumph practically within his grasp, Kelly, with his young helper, quickly scaled the rock wall to the top of the big boulder, and prepared to descend to the nesting cave. The long effort to prove his integrity and the true origin and identity of his condor egg was near success. While Dawson got photographic documentation of the condor and the nest location, all that remained to complete the proof was to find a big creamy-white egg in the cave below.

With my brother holding the rope, and with the two-pound coffee can again buttoned safely inside the front of his shirt, Truesdale lowered himself toward the nest. As he slid downward, his foot dislodged a small stone that bounced past the opening in the face of the rock. At this disturbance a strange sound came from inside the cavity. At first it startled Kelly; then his eager confidence changed to a sickening feeling of dread. Repeated at quick intervals, the sound was a snakelike hiss followed by a rasping grunt. Something more than a condor egg was in the cave.

As he reached the mouth of the cave, the frightening sound increased. He put his head inside to investigate. One quick glance confirmed his fear. Near the far wall, hissing and grunting in a ferocious manner far out of keeping with its size and apparent strength, was a nestling condor. The trip of confirmation and vindication was too late. Ruefully, in a voice that was anything but triumphant, Kelly called to Dawson to come up and witness the evidence of disaster. At least he could prove that his condor nest was active and occupied.

Dawson soon gained the top of the great boulder and climbed down with Truesdale to examine the nest and its occupant. The young condor had evidently been hatched for several days. Though its flesh-colored head and neck were naked, it was otherwise covered almost entirely with a coat of fluffy white down. Although weak and helpless in appearance, with its frightful voice and generally hostile attitude it was obviously doing everything possible to ward off this invasion of its nest.

The two men noted also that the parent bird still perched on the nearby point. Its great height, almost four feet, was impressive at such a short distance, and in marked contrast to the weak and helpless appearance of the nestling. How long, they wondered, would it take such a feeble little creature to grow into a great bird like the one perched nearby? How could it be explained that young condors, before they could even walk, could recognize an enemy and make such startling, ferocious sounds?

For several minutes Dawson commiserated with Kelly over the crushing misfortune of the hatched egg. So close to victory, the failure was all the more insufferable. At last, as they were about to leave, Kelly, in a random gesture of despair, picked up a large pebble that lay near the entrance of the nest and tossed it toward the young condor. At this, the belligerent nestling shifted its position slightly, and as it did so the two men could see on the sandy floor of the cave a white object that previously had been hidden behind the young bird. In an instant Truesdale was inside. Although the chick struck at him with its beak as he reached near, he was quickly back with Dawson, bringing with him the white object. It was a large segment of eggshell, obviously part of the egg from which the young condor had been hatched.

In the sunlight at the entrance of the cave, the two men examined the shell closely. Somewhat different in color from the usual greenish-white of most condor eggs, it was creamy white. On this proof, together with the fact of the occupied nest, Dawson said that he would now confirm and verify Kelly's unsold condor egg as being genuine. At this assertion the wild canyon echoed, as it had on a previous occasion, to the piercing yell of a jubilant egg collector.

From all the records that Carl Koford could find in his study of condor history, the highest price ever paid for a condor egg was the $300 received by Kelly Truesdale from John E. Thayer. Finally, with fame and fortune at least temporarily won, Kelly would return each February, season after season, a bearded harbinger of springtime in the condor country, to exploit his discovery further.

From 1908, when his first egg was collected, Kelly took a total of five condor eggs from this same nesting territory, the last being taken in 1920. All went to private collectors outside California. Amazingly, two eggs hatched during this twelve-year period, the one of Dawson's visit, and another when snow and ice on the nesting cliff made it impossible to reach the top of the big boulder. The condors, in this last retreat, with no alternative left, were persistent and to some extent successful.

In one season following the Dawson expedition, the intrigue that seemed to characterize oological activities again brought cruel disillusionment to Kelly. On this occasion the condors were found nesting at a new location not far from the old site. Before taking the egg, Kelly Truesdale decided the new nest should be photographed. Having no camera, he left a collector who had accompanied him on this particular expedition to watch the camp until his return. It took five days to go back to Shandon, take a horse-drawn stage from there to Paso Robles, buy a camera and film, and return to the wilderness camp. Tired but eager, on the afternoon of the fifth day Kelly rode into the little clearing where his colleague had been left to await his return. He looked about expectantly. With no one in sight he shouted; but there was only silence from the surrounding chaparral. Then he noticed that the belongings of his associate were gone. At this discovery he quickly went to the grub box in which, along with provisions for the camp, other needed items were kept.

Here his suspicion was further confirmed; the two-pound coffee can filled with cotton was also missing.

Tired but indomitable, Kelly, with a length of rope, climbed the trail toward the condor nest. There was no sign of condors in the wild canyon as he reached the foot of the towering rock wall. Located on a ledge, the new site was more easily reached than the cave in the face of the big boulder. Truesdale climbed to a point above, and roped down. When he examined the sandy floor where the big egg had been, he found only a few wisps of white cotton. His trusted colleague had been careful with the treasure.

Another year, when the condors again nested on this same ledge, Kelly found a condor on the nest incubating the egg. When it left, the big egg was brought to the edge of the ledge, only to topple to the rocks below. It splattered near where Kelly was standing. Of his many experiences in the wild canyon, the sight of the splattering condor egg would remain in Kelly's memory as the most excruciating and unforgettable.

Chapter IV

KELLY'S NEST
REVISITED

ONE DAY IN THE SPRING OF 1946, AS I WAS DOING chores on my ranch in the Red Hills, a rather dilapidated car drove up, and a lean but well-built youth, who turned out to be older than he looked, got out and introduced himself. It was Carl Koford, recently home from service in World War II, who was resuming the condor study that had been interrupted in 1941 by the war. Spring was in the air, and the situation was somehow reminiscent of former days, when Kelly Truesdale would arrive at the old homestead in McMillan Canyon with intriguing reports of his collecting adventures.

When Koford came to see me in the Red Hills, he was in the last stages of his study. The year before, my brother-in-law, Carl Twisselman, had found the carcass of a dead condor near a stock-watering site on his ranch in the Temblor Range on the east side of the

Carrisa Plains. I had taken the specimen to the Museum of Natural History in Santa Barbara, and a report of the incident had appeared in *The Condor*. Koford had read it and had come to inquire about the dead bird.

After I had told him what I knew about the condor, I took Carl Koford on a tour of the neighborhood. We visited two occupied golden-eagle nests, one in a high cliff, the other in a big oak. From a high point of the Red Hills, I pointed out the bluff where Kelly Truesdale's historic condor nest was located. Northward from this same point we could see the big Cholame Flat where condors had been appearing in recent years.

Koford stayed overnight at the ranch, and on the following day we ranged over a wider portion of the Shandon region. When he left, it was agreed that he would return later in the spring, so that we could investigate the recent appearance of condors in the Shandon area, where the big birds had never been seen in the days when Kelly Truesdale was hunting for their eggs. We also planned to visit the old nesting site in the wild canyon on the west of the Carrisa.

A few months later, we made our trip to Kelly Truesdale's historic condor nest. An extensive forest fire had swept over the area seven years earlier, and except for scattered patches, the chaparral had been burned off, leaving a stand of bare stumps and branches.

However, the brush had already well recovered from this burn, and again formed a barricade against easy access into the wild canyon. But the bulldozer, now a common implement of forest management, had scraped open trails and roadways here and there through the cover. No longer was it necessary to use an ax to reach the old nest.

On our way in, passing near the campsite where Kelly and his partner had watched the condors over thirty years earlier, we noted the remains of a mine that had operated here at some time during the California Gold Rush. According to local history an encampment of Chinese miners worked the gravel of the wild canyon decades before Kelly arrived in search of the condor's nest. In passing these old diggings, we speculated whether condors had been here with the miners, and if so, how they had got along.

It was still early in the forenoon when we came in good view of the high bluff above the old nest. Through our binoculars we studied a small group of turkey vultures that were soaring above the cliffs. Koford gave a short exclamation. He had spotted a lone adult condor perched on one of the higher rocks, its bare, bright-colored head glistening in the morning sun. Perhaps the old nest was still in use. A few minutes after we came in sight, the condor took flight and spiraled upward with no more than a few strokes of the wings. The morning sun was warming the air, and the rising thermals offered good soaring conditions. In a few minutes the gliding figure had disappeared out toward its ancestral feeding grounds on the open Carrisa.

An hour later, Koford, an expert mountaineer, reached the great boulder midway of the rock bluff, and with the use of a light rope went down to the historic cave. It was unoccupied, and he found no evidence that condors had used it during the previous year or two. However, the lower portions of the cave wall were whitewashed with condor excrement, evidence of quite extensive use at some time in the not too distant past.

In examining the nest cave the young zoologist measured the rather small entrance. As noted later in his report, this opening was given as 15 inches high and 17 inches across. Dawson had observed in his visit of 1911 that it was an actual squeeze for the condor to get out through the nest entrance. He gave the exact size of the opening as being 12 inches high and 19 inches wide. He also pointed out that the condors, in struggling through the opening, had broken out portions of the sides.

The greater height of this opening as found by Koford, thirty-five years after Dawson's measurement, could possibly have been caused by the condors continuing to break out the thin edges of the hole. But the width of the aperture could not have shrunk, as it would necessarily have had to do if Dawson's early measurement of 19 inches and Koford's later one of 17 were both accurate.

It may appear trifling and irrelevant to be pointing out this odd discrepancy of two inches in the measurements of the entrance to a condor nest. If Dawson's figures were not exact, it seems only fair to recall that in 1911 Joseph Grinnell's institution of scientific research on the Berkeley campus was only just beginning to function. At that time how would two egg collectors at the entrance of a remote condor nest suspect that a generation later their measurements would be called into question by the accuracy of observation stressed in Grinnell's teaching?

With Koford I speculated on whether the wild canyon was still a suitable place for condors to nest. As Kelly Truesdale and his partner had found, the old nesting territory was a good place to learn and think about condors. The towering rock wall was unchanged from the time I had first seen it on a memorable collecting expedition with Kelly back in 1921. The brush fire of seven years before had not reached the more scattered trees and shrubs on the higher cliffs. In itself this fire would probably not have seriously affected condors nesting in the old cave. On the slopes below the nest, the chaparral was already closing in again as a protective shield against easy human access.

In the vicinity of the old nest, the only new feature that might affect its suitability as condor habitat was the bulldozer trail we had followed to the foot of the nesting bluff.

By 1946 the bulldozer, a new implement of road building and brush clearance, had opened up extensive areas of previously inaccessible wild lands in the condor range to motorized travel. World War II was over, and four-wheel-drive vehicles were commonly available for purposes of traveling almost anywhere that a bulldozer could make a roadway. In but a year or two the jeep had become a popular mode of travel in hunting deer. Men home from the armed forces were nearly all trained in the use of the rifle. A great many were eager to hunt. The migration of people to California from other regions had increased during and after the war. The deer population had grown in the condor country, and economic conditions were favorable for a boom in hunting. The range of the condor, most of which is in Los Padres National Forest, became a main center of the new hunting boom.

Looking down from our position near the old nest, we considered the probable effect of this bulldozed roadway on the welfare of condors. In August, when deer season opened, it would be dangerous for any large bird to perch on the high rock where we had seen the condor a couple of hours before. Parent condors bringing food to a nestling in the cave near where we sat would be tempting targets to irresponsible riflemen. In September the hunting season would still be open. Young condors would then be out of the nest, but flightless. Both the juvenile and its parents would be exposed to the kind of shooting that had been a main cause of condor mortality since men with guns first appeared in the condor country.

At the moment the nearest sign of human activity in the open country beyond was the dust of a tractor on one of the big wheat ranches, fifteen miles away on the broad Carrisa. A more distant cloud of dust rose where a big band of sheep was moving down a canyon in the Temblor Range. The sheep and cattle grazing on that vast stretch of open country were a source of food for the successful rearing of a young condor. No condor nest, however ideal it might otherwise be, could function successfully without such a food supply, consistently available throughout the year and within daily cruising range of a pair of the great scavengers.

The productive soil of those open ranges had for thousands of years supported a wealth of animal life. Before the coming of the white man, a host of grazing mammals, including antelope, deer, and elk, had supported a dependent population of predators, including the native Indian. All but the Indian had provided carrion for the condors.

But since the European settlers had arrived, the antelope had practically disappeared, the elk had dwindled to a remnant herd or two, and intensive hunting by the homesteaders of Kelly Truesdale's time had also decimated the deer. The grizzly bear, common fifty years earlier in the woodlands of oak and digger pine that fringed and intermingled with the chaparral, was gone. However, the domestic livestock of the white man now provided a food supply for the condor probably never equaled in aboriginal times.

The paradox of condor ecology and survival could be studied in detail from our lookout above the wild canyon. Wild, inaccessible mountain retreats for nesting, roosting, and general safety can function to advantage only if they lie within range of extensive foraging grounds. Conversely, the food on the fertile ranges, however abundant it might be, is of little avail to condors without the retreats in the wilderness.

In the period of about forty years since Kelly Truesdale had seen his first condor gliding over the Carrisa, the area had undergone profound ecological change. With the advent of mechanized farming and transportation, the former expanse of grassland, with only a few scattered pieces under cultivation, had in four decades been converted into a great patchwork of wheatfields. Although the farmlands were also grazed, the production of condor food would be considerably different from what it was before.

However, most of the ranchlands surrounding the level plain were too wooded, steep, or arid for cultivated crops. These were still pastured in much the same way as in previous decades. This grazing, as it had continued from the days of early settlement, was typically excessive. Its early effects were confirmed in the historic droughts of the middle and late 1800's when great numbers of livestock died from starvation.

In the early stages of this overstocking, the native perennial grasses of the semiarid region were demolished. With this stable type of forage gone, a weedy annual growth was produced each year that fluctuated in abundance according to the widely fluctuating rainfall. The average annual rainfall on the Carrisa Plains of about ten inches varied from year to year between extremes of around five and twenty inches. On an occasional dry year some areas already bare from overgrazing remained bare from lack of rain. This contributed to range mortality and the production of condor food.

By 1946 new means of transportation made possible the quick and extensive movement of livestock, and also made feasible the use of supplemental feed. Being able to move stock quickly from regions of range shortage to areas where conditions were better further intensified the excessive grazing. To be caught with hungry livestock in times of drought no longer meant disaster. Feed could be brought in or the stock taken elsewhere.

Where too many animals had grazed the delicate, semiarid ranges for at least a century, the new facilities now made it profitable to stock more animals and accelerate the depletion. This was another phase in the maximum exploitation of a new, rich country already growing old and worn out from excessive use. But as paradox would again have it, these range practices, intended to be sound and highly efficient, led toward increased livestock mortality, and what first appeared as practices that would reduce the supply of condor food, in a few years were causing it to rise.

Although advancement in veterinarian services had brought under control the two deadly livestock diseases, anthrax and blackleg, new problems arose. Contagious abortion, pinkeye, anaplasmosis, leptospirosis, and septicemia were among the increasing causes of livestock death in the 1940's.

Furthermore, in the continuing range depletion, plants poisonous or injurious to livestock increased. A tall species of larkspur that becomes toxic at a certain stage of growth became a common cause of cattle death on the ranges surrounding the Carrisa. Locoweed, another injurious forage plant, throve. In some seasons an abnormal amount of nitrate in the annual growth on some ranges caused it to become poisonous to cattle.

Although it was the popular impression that range mortality had been reduced, it was actually increasing. The lone condor we had seen glide out toward the Carrisa the morning of our visit would probably find as wide a choice of available carcasses as condors had found thirty years earlier. Perhaps the supply of condor food was as plentiful on this day in 1946 as at any time in the days before the white man, when the elk, the antelope, and the California grizzly ran free on the open Carrisa.

In reviewing this trip to Kelly's old condor nest, I should mention that at this time in 1946 the condor population may well have been at its highest peak in decades. In the previous year Eugene Percy saw a flock of forty-two condors on his ranch near the Sespe Refuge. In 1947, Perry Sprague, foreman on the Tejon Ranch, counted forty-three birds in one gathering. In his thirty years at the big ranch, this was the largest group Sprague had seen. In 1947, when I was again in the area of the old Truesdale nest, I watched fourteen condors leave a roosting site there. Kelly in all his condor observations of former decades never saw more than five birds at any one time.

Chapter V

NEW DISCOVERIES

AFTER THE VISIT TO THE OLD NEST SITE, I took Carl Koford on another trip to a place about twelve miles north of my ranch where condors had surprisingly appeared in the 1940's. Rancho Cholame covers about 50,000 acres. It is mainly rolling hill country typical of the stock ranges over which the condors do most of their foraging. It includes one of the few land grants, possibly the only one that remains intact from the time of Mexican ownership of California and the era of the big ranchos. Centrally located in this ranch is a big flat about seven miles long and two miles wide. Except for the ranch headquarters and a field of irrigated cropland, this big flat is open range.

McMillan Canyon, where I grew up, is a few miles west of the Cholame Flat. In the 1920's the region was well populated with golden eagles; and one spring Kelly Truesdale, with one of my older brothers, collected thirty-four sets of eagle eggs. But Truesdale never saw a condor here then, nor did my father, who was an active hunter and had arrived in McMillan Canyon as a young home- steader in 1884.

It was of particular note, therefore, when condors were first seen in the Cholame area in the early 1940's. In 1941, a ranch hand found a dead condor in a water tank about twelve miles from the big ranch. The specimen was mounted and placed on display at Fresno State College. In 1944, a group of twenty condors was seen on the Cholame Flat, and reported in due course in *The Condor*.

On June 1, 1945, while at the Shandon post office, I learned from a rancher acquaintance that less than an hour before he had seen a group of condors at a carcass on the Cholame Flat. Hurrying to the spot with a few other interested persons, I saw the first condors I had ever seen except in the area of Kelly Truesdale's nest. Thirteen of the great birds were gathered at the carcass of a dead cow. As we approached, they scrambled into the air and wheeled upward over the open flat.

These appearances in an area where condors had never been known to occur before were at first considered to be vagrant wanderings from their usual range some forty miles to the south. When I went with Carl Koford to the Cholame Ranch in June of 1946, there had been no reports of condors in the area that year. We were naturally surprised to find a flock of ten foraging about over the big flat. Watching the birds as they left in late afternoon, we followed their straight glide until they disappeared in the direction of Castle Mountain, the highest, most remote elevation in the region. This high piece of back country lies about twelve miles north of the Cholame Ranch. Obviously the condors were roosting in that still remote, wild section and were using the surrounding stock range as a new foraging ground.

This was a new development, and Koford was eager to give it a thorough investigation. Early the next morning we were back on the big flat, watching a calf carcass that we had seen the day before. In the annual roundup and branding operations on the old rancho, some calves usually died from castration or other injuries, and this contributed to the supply of condor food.

Using our parked car as a blind, we watched as condors appeared over the carcass near the edge of the open flat. One at a time, at intervals of a minute or so, they sailed in on set wings, all following the same course from the direction of Castle Mountain. As they approached, we could see that their legs were extended in a hanging position. Condors characteristically lower their legs several minutes before landing. This may serve as a brake or balance in slowing and stabilizing the descending flight of the twenty-pound birds.

Circling in slow, lowering flight, the great vultures landed near the dead calf that was still being watched over by the mother cow. In less than half an hour ten had arrived, the same number we had seen the day before. The condors seemed to show little or no awareness of our car, which was parked about half a mile away. With the cow on guard they did not feed, but nonetheless remained in the immediate area of the carcass until midafternoon, engaging in a wide variety of interesting behavior.

There was water near the carcass—a sort of bog from the overflow of a spring. The condors seemed to be attracted to this spot, some of them evidently drinking or perhaps attempting to bathe. A considerable amount of squabbling and fighting took place among the birds as they walked and stood about, evidently expecting to feed on the dead calf. At intervals one bird would dash at another, reaching out with its bill. Sometimes the two combatants would stand their ground for a time, pecking and jumping at each other with wings beating until one yielded. Upraised wings seemed to be gestures of either threat or defense. In this posture the wings of a standing condor may reach to a height of around six feet, giving the bird a most formidable appearance.

Watching this interplay of attack and retreat, as the hours passed we noted that an order of dominance, or rank, emerged. At least two of the birds were dark-headed immatures under six years old. These were evidently the lowest in rank. They retreated in all their encounters with adult birds. However, they fought vigorously with each other. But the youngest, which was all dark in plumage, always retreated in the end.

Two of the adult birds were evidently high in the peck order. They were never challenged when they threatened other members of the flock. Although this was undoubtedly a group of nonbreeding birds, these two high-ranking adults might have been a mated pair that had failed in a nesting effort earlier in the spring. In the long testing of condor survival, it has evidently been of advantage for non-nesting birds to organize into social groups with each member having a particular rank. This would provide for the continued guidance and training of immature condors until they are on their own as paired adults.

Impatience at not being able to feed may have caused some of the antagonism among the condors. Although the calf had been dead about two days, the mother cow stayed in the immediate territory. She would graze off for some distance, then return. When the cow moved away the condors, standing expectantly nearby, would advance toward the dead calf. Once, one of the birds got so far as to stand on the carcass. At this approach by the big scavengers, the cow would return and the vultures would back off a few yards while the cow eyed them anxiously. In moving back before the cow's advance, the condors would raise their wings upright, thus appearing much larger and more impressive even than their normal four-foot stature. It was a moving sight to watch the bereaved cow stand at the bloated carcass of her calf, holding off the vultures as they stood near in a rough semicircle, some with upraised wings, waiting expectantly.

In midafternoon, as the cow remained on guard, one of the adult condors with a leaping run over the level terrain took flight, first flapping heavily, then soaring in ascending circles. In ten minutes it appeared to be at least half a mile above the flat. At that height, with a dip of the wings, its circling changed to a straight, steady glide toward the north and the remote mountain where the birds had evidently roosted the night before.

By the time this leader was fading out of sight, all other members of the flock but one were also on the wing and following the same course. The last one to leave was the black immature. Perhaps in its ordered place in the group this young bird was allowed at the carcass only after the others had fed. In this instance, however, the mother cow nullified the entire feeding procedure. She was still faithfully on guard as the black bird finally spiraled upward and lined out toward the distant mountain.

Considering that the condors would be unusually hungry the following day, and that the cow might no longer be staying near the remains of her calf, we again traveled early to our observation point. The cow was gone and a few ravens were at the carcass when we arrived. At about the same time as we had first seen one of the birds the previous morning, a condor, first appearing in our binoculars as a speck above the outline of the far peak, came over and began to circle. Soon nine had arrived, one less than the day before. With all the birds soaring in wide circles over the location, it appeared almost certain that we were about to observe a condor feast.

As we watched and waited for the condors to land, it became obvious that they were not going to do so as readily as on the previous day. Occasionally one would descend as if to alight, then flap heavily upward and rejoin the circling flock. Finally, to our surprise and disappointment, an adult, which was soaring above the rest, lined out in a glide toward the southeast, with the rest of the flock following in more or less single file. First through our binoculars, then through the telescope, we followed this unwavering flight until the last condor had disappeared some eight miles in the distance.

Perplexed, we deliberated on the meaning of this strange development and how it might be further studied. Koford was the least surprised. In his extensive observations he had found it impossible to predict whether condors will feed on a certain carcass on a certain day. He told of various efforts made by photographers to bait condors. In some of these attempts, after waiting for days without success and after the project was given up, condors had subsequently devoured the bait. In one of the few successful attempts to photograph feeding condors, J. R. Pemberton, a pioneer member of the Cooper Ornithological Club, attempted baiting more than thirty times before a feeding group was photographed.

We wondered how far they might travel in their set glide toward the southeast. It was almost forty miles in that direction to the old nest site on the west of the Carrisa. It was sixty-five miles from the Cholame Ranch to Sisquoc Canyon. If they had come from a roost on Castle Mountain, they had traveled at least twelve miles to reach the Cholame Flat and over twenty when they passed from our sight. Were they moving to another local foraging ground or traveling back to their traditional centers of activity?

The possibility of another local foraging area reminded me of a sheep ranch that was located in the area toward which the flock had headed. Mutton is a preferred condor food, as we knew, and I suggested that in following the course taken by the birds we might find them in the territory of the sheep ranch. To attempt to follow and locate a group of foraging condors in the vast expanse of hill country of eastern San Luis Obispo County was indeed an optimistic venture. But optimism was ours as we headed southeast as fast as the range roads would permit.

We traveled slightly over twenty miles to a point in good view of the sheep range, which was located at the western edge of the San Joaquin Valley. As we stopped on one of the higher points to look for soaring birds, we first studied briefly the vast scene toward the east. About every form of land use was represented in the sixty-mile stretch across the level floor of the great valley. Irrigated crops, mainly of fruit, cotton, grain, and alfalfa, covered much of the central portion. The derricks of an oil field stood out plainly. At different points we could locate centers of population that had grown rapidly during the past few years as people migrated westward from the Dust Bowl. The great drought of the 1930's had caused extensive migration into the San Joaquin.

Oddly, however, this great level patchwork of farmland, oil fields, and urban development was bordered by an almost uninterrupted strip of stock range. Underground water supplies and the extensive irrigation systems of the region were generally restricted to the central portions of the big valley. Since the semiarid climate was unfavorable for dry farming, livestock grazing prevailed almost exclusively as the principal form of agriculture along the bordering foothills.

The hilly, semiarid sheep range we had come to investigate was typical of this bordering strip as it extended along the west side of the valley. Sixty miles away on the east side we could barely make out this same border of rangeland as it lay between the level lowlands and the upper slopes of the Sierra Nevada. On this hot day in late June the air was clear. Dim in the distance, the forested slopes of the Sierra Nevada appeared like a long band of blue above the tawny foothill range. Above that, a jagged line of snowcapped peaks rimmed the eastern horizon. It was a scene that could distract the attention even of an eager party of condor watchers.

Koford was now engaged in determining the size and distribution of the condor population and the current limits of the species' range. The evidence he had gathered showed a range in 1946 generally limited to a crescent-shaped territory a little over two hundred miles from south to north, with its southern limits in southern Ventura

County. From there the range broadened toward the north and branched around the southern rim of the San Joaquin Valley into two long, narrow arms of condor territory. These northern arms of the condor range are separated by the valley. Condors evidently do not fly across this sixty-mile-wide expanse of level country.

Within the general limits of this range, the areas of main condor activity had changed considerably in recent decades. For instance, while condor activity appeared to be lowering in the Sisquoc region during the early 1940's, the species appeared quite commonly on the Cholame Ranch in northeastern San Luis Obispo County where it had not been seen before. During this period, also, more condors appeared along the east side of the southern San Joaquin Valley, mainly on the big Tejon Ranch.

What causes these shifts in condor distribution is a prime question of wildlife research. Its answer undoubtedly lies in the realm of ecology—the relationship between the species and its environment. It was into this complex realm that Koford's research was probing.

Within view from our location was a major portion of the occupied condor range that Koford had been exploring. Mainly foraging ground, it included the great horseshoe of range country that bordered the southern end of the San Joaquin. Due east across the valley Koford had recently found a group of condors feeding on poisoned ground squirrels. A main question to be answered was whether those birds could have moved in a short time to the Cholame area and be the same condors we were following. Only sixty miles across the valley floor, it would be around three times that distance by way of the strip of hill country around the southern rim.

Bringing our attention back to the local sheep range, we scanned the surrounding horizon for large birds. Ravens were common in this area, nesting in rock cliffs that occurred in several places along the edge of the lowlands. Turkey vultures and prairie falcons also nested in these outcrops. Swainson hawks, common in the region years before, were now rare, but an occasional nesting pair still remained. Jack rabbits were plentiful in the lowlands, making this a favorite hunting ground for golden eagles. Red-tailed hawks also ranged the area.

With Koford, myself, and my twelve-year-old son making an observation party of three, we discussed the distinguishing features of the larger birds that came in view. Koford had been at this work for several years, and was an expert. In looking for condors, it is important to identify all birds that at a distance could appear to be the size of a condor. Adult golden eagles on the wing at a distance of a mile or more appear in size and color much the same as do young condors in the dark phase of plumage. Turkey vultures present somewhat the same problem. To be positive about the identification of a raven soaring two miles away, it is necessary to employ criteria other than size or color. Some Swainson hawks, otherwise dark in plumage, may have white patches under the wings resembling those of condors. At great distances this plumage pattern can be confusing.

But after all the identification marks and other peculiarities are learned, accuracy as a condor watcher may still be lacking. The sense of perception varies widely in different people. It seems that the only way to be sure of a person's ability to identify condors at a distance is to be in the field with that person and note his identification of birds that could possibly be mistaken for condors. If, using binoculars of about seven power, he distinguishes accurately between a golden eagle and a turkey vulture on the wing at a distance of around two miles, and between a red-tailed and a Swainson hawk at a mile, he should pass as a dependable condor watcher.

After several minutes of looking around without seeing condors, we drove on toward another section of the sheep ranch. The range road, after leaving a ridge, followed along the floor of a canyon. We had seen several ravens and a few turkey vultures, and were carefully examining each distant bird. Ahead of us, as we drove along, a large bird appeared, rising in wide circles from the floor of the canyon. At a distance of about half a mile, and even from our traveling car, we could see that it was a condor. We stopped and quickly put our binoculars on the spiraling bird, which was now being joined in its rising flight by several others. The birds had been on the ground, apparently at a carcass. Eight birds were now in the air, with one remaining on the ground. As we examined this last bird, it walked rapidly several yards up the side of the canyon, and in a short downhill run launched into flight. It appeared to be the same black immature that had been the last to leave the carcass on the Cholame Flat the day before.

Watching the soaring vultures as they circled rapidly upward and

7., 8., 9. and 10. The adult condor's soaring flight.

11. and 12.
Coming in to
land.

were gone, we reflected on the role of this last young lagging bird. Although we had frightened the birds from the carcass, this had not upset the order in which the youngest was again the last to leave. This natural rank, or status, called the "peck order," has been studied extensively by ornithologists. It is evidently a product of natural selection operating as an agent of survival. In our two days of observing this flock of condors, the function of this peck order seemed obvious. It would assure that the breeding stock of adult birds on which reproduction depended would not be risked in favor of immatures that might not yet be able to survive without the guidance and teaching of the older, more experienced condors. It also assured that the available supply of condor food would be distributed so that shortage, if it should occur, would affect only the number of birds in excess of what could be adequately fed. This would protect the population from the mass starvation that could occur if a food supply sufficient for a certain number was distributed equally among a greater number.

With this peck order functioning as a procedure for optimum distribution of food, the existence of the immature black bird confirmed the presence of an adequate food supply. In being lowest in rank and the last of the flock to feed, the fact of its survival was proof that the entire flock had been feeding well. This was an important consideration to keep in mind when assessing condor food. Starvation could hardly be a problem in a condor population that included strong, healthy immatures.

After the condors had left, we drove to the spot where they had been gathered. On the way, we debated as to what they might have been eating. In approaching the site we could see no sheep carcass. Jack rabbits were common, and a few ground squirrels still remained after several years of a regional squirrel-poisoning campaign. This rodent poisoning had practically extirpated the coyotes of the region through secondary poisoning. But the little desert kit fox, ranging the more arid areas where the poisoning had not been so extensive, was still present in fair numbers. This was good badger country, but deer rarely ranged so far from wooded areas. Making hypothetical wagers as to the carcass we expected to find, each of us picked the food species we considered to be the most probable. A lamb, a jack rabbit, and a ground squirrel were the three choices. Getting out of the car, we found what first appeared to be the remains of a coyote but on closer examination turned out to be a small brindle sheep dog the condors had picked clean. I learned later from the sheep rancher that poisoned grain had recently been put out for ground squirrels and that the little dog had evidently eaten a poisoned rodent.

The strange propensity of condors to do the unexpected and inexplicable had been dramatically confirmed in our day's observations. Surprised that the birds had left a well-supplied feeding site, we had been further surprised to be able to follow and find them. But we were even more surprised at their final choice of food. Why would a group of hungry vultures leave the calf carcass on the Cholame Flat to travel over twenty miles to feed on a small dog? Their behavior impressed upon us the need for skepticism and caution in arriving at conclusions; they cultivated the humility needed for objective observation and thought.

Of the various condor flights that Koford had been able to measure, this long cruise of about thirty-five miles from Castle Mountain to the far sheep ranch was the greatest. To locate and examine the roosting site, he drove the following day to the end of a road on the south side of that mountain. Sleeping there and hiking on early the next morning, he found the roosting birds perched in a grove of pines on the north side of the peak. This was at the head of a rugged canyon, the most isolated and primitive spot in all the region.

After his condor research was well completed, Carl Koford returned to the Red Hills at various times. The condors were still showing up on the Cholame Ranch, and occasionally we toured that interesting area to look for them. In 1947 we saw a flock of twenty-two on the big flat, the largest group I have ever seen and the largest on record for this part of the species' range.

In 1950, while Koford's report was still in preparation, word reached the Museum of Vertebrate Zoology that a pair of condors had been found nesting in a cavity of a giant sequoia tree in the mountains of Tulare County on the east side of the San Joaquin Valley. There were no previous records of tree nests or of condors nesting in the region on the east side of the Great Valley. The report seemed incredible. But in making a trip to the location, Koford found it to be true. The big tree was about 170 feet tall and 15 feet in diameter. A large cavity almost 100 feet above the ground was the occupied nest. Again condors had done what they had never been known to do before.

In September, after his first investigation of this tree nest, Koford came to the Red Hills, and my brother Eben and I accompanied him on a second trip to observe it. The young bird would soon be leaving the nest, and information about this was important. Entering the Tule Indian Reservation where the nest was located, we followed a new logging road that had been bulldozed out of the timbered mountainsides. About twenty-five miles of this steep, rough roadway took us to a recently established lumber camp. The nesting tree was about 200 feet off the new roadway and about a quarter of a mile from the camp. In the lumbering operations workmen had noticed feathers on the ground near the big tree and, looking up, had sighted one of the condors. The discovery was a notable event in the field of natural history, and received wide publicity.

To determine whether the young bird was still in the nest, we enlisted the help of Claude Rouch, Jr., foreman of the lumbering operations. Climbing an occasional big tree was part of his lumbering work. With ropes, belts, and climbing spikes, Rouch and my brother Eben, also an expert climber, went up a tall pine that grew near the nesting tree. Reaching a height opposite the nesting cavity, one of them gave a shout of surprise. Partially hidden by several branches, the young condor, now almost full grown, was perched on a limb that extended out toward them. No more than about thirty feet from the two climbers, the big young bird watched them quietly, seemingly without concern.

This tree nest was given special evaluation in Koford's report. Explaining the proximity of the nest to the lumbering operations, he pointed out that this single, odd instance could not be used as evidence that human activity near nest sites is harmless to condors. At an elevation of 6,500 feet, snow causes the territory to be isolated from human activity each winter and spring during the early months of the nesting cycle. High within the forest canopy, the nest was generally hidden from the nearby roadway.

This cavity in the big tree could well have been unique as the only suitable nest site in the region. Located in a remote part of the Indian reservation, prior to the lumbering project the site had been generally isolated from human disturbance. On the north-facing side of a canyon, it was sheltered from prevailing storms; and the cavity, also facing northward, was also protected. A large limb grew from the main trunk, just below the next cavity. This provided a perch from which the adults could enter the nest. The young bird could also perch on this limb in its flightless stage after first leaving the nest.

This cavity in the side of the giant sequoia offered the same practical advantages as the face of a high cliff. Although quite a distance by the new road, it was only a few miles by condor flight to the extensive foothill range below and the necessary food supply. Appraising the general situation, we found a remarkable parallel in which the prerequisites of a condor-nesting territory were represented here much the same as in the wild canyon where Kelly Truesdale's historic nest was located. There was an equally striking parallel in the bulldozed roadways that we had followed to each retreat.

However, the main significance of this discovery was not in evidence at the time of our first investigation in 1950. The evidence on which finally to evaluate this nesting situation was gathered thirteen years later in our 1963–1964 survey. Returning to the big tree in October of 1963, my brother and I examined the ground below the cavity for evidence of condors. In 1950 we had found an assortment of feathers and regurgitated bones scattered about under the nest. In this later visit there was no such evidence.

Seeking information of any recent nestings, we talked with different Indians on the reservation who had seen the condors in 1950 and were interested in them. According to them, condors had continued to appear in the territory as late as 1954, but we could find no credible evidence that the nest was used after the 1950 discovery. Evidently, as had happened in practically every known nesting area outside the remaining mountain retreats in Ventura and Santa Barbara counties, when their nesting territory was invaded by human beings the condors had left.

In 1963 the lumbering project had been completed for several years, but the bulldozed road still made the area easily accessible by car. The abandoned lumber camp was now used by the Indians as a hunting headquarters. We saw many signs of target shooting, and a dead red-tailed hawk lay at the roadside near the old nest.

Prior to the lumbering project, probably no spot along the entire west front of the Sierra Nevada at this elevation would have been safer from human encroachment. Within the Indian Reservation, industry and development had not operated so freely and extensively as on other lands of the condor range. If a pair of condors could find nesting seclusion anywhere, it would seem to be here. But even here the bulldozer and economics could not be denied. Even where it required twenty-five miles of bulldozed roadway to reach the only place that condors had been known to nest in this entire region, that place had been reached and ruined.

Chapter VI

THE REAPPRAISAL
of 1963-1964

ALTHOUGH MY BROTHER AND I WERE QUALI-
fied by location and experience to gather the evidence of condor
status, we were not professional zoologists, and needed help in the
technical aspects of the proposed study. Alden Miller was probably
the most accomplished ornithologist of his day. Having directed
Carl Koford's condor study, he was an authority on condor research.
This qualified him beyond question for the responsibility of planning and directing the new appraisal.

We decided that a period of at least eighteen months would be
required to gather the necessary field information, and another six
months to prepare the report. Beginning in February of 1963, this
period would span two nesting seasons. Condors normally nest
every two years, so that most of the breeding pairs would probably

nest on one or the other of the two seasons, and make possible a general appraisal of reproduction.

As the life history of the condor had been thoroughly studied and reported on by Carl Koford, our survey could concentrate on the species' status and welfare. It was of first importance to determine as nearly as possible the number of living condors and to evaluate the various factors affecting nesting and rearing success. Food would be assessed at every opportunity. Disturbance in their mountain retreats and the effects of hunting on the condor were important. We would need to appraise the official administration of the condor program.

After working for years to help build a program of condor preservation, my brother and I were excited by this new opportunity. To us the condor had come to represent the kind of country in which we had grown up and to which we felt that we also belonged. The more we had come to know the great birds, the more they seemed to need and deserve our help and protection. As in former years, when Kelly Truesdale and later Carl Koford would come with their propositions, we again put aside what ranch duties could be postponed and eagerly went to work on the new adventure with the condors.

To cover the entire condor range as completely and as thoroughly as possible, we recruited a force of volunteer observers, people living in the condor country who were interested in the birds and were strategically located to see them. Ranchers, sportsmen, sheepherders, wildlife officials, forest rangers, and others participated in the survey. Condor sightings were reported to our central positions by mail if they were of no exceptional significance. If something special was noted, such as large gatherings or evidence of disabled or dead birds, we were to be reached by telephone as soon as possible.

This wide coverage enabled us to focus our own field observations on the situations that seemed to offer the most in the way of needed information. The death of a condor on the east side of the San Joaquin Valley a hundred miles from our somewhat central location in the Red Hills; three birds seen in San Benito County a hundred miles to the north; a group of twenty-two condors reported foraging over a ranch in the Simi Valley of southern Ventura County, over a hundred airline miles to the south—all could receive our immediate attention.

Our first and perhaps most important trip was to the ranch of Eugene Percy in the mountains on the south boundary of the Sespe Condor Sanctuary. Condors roosting or nesting in the sanctuary commonly forage over this area, and so their numbers could be determined. We could identify young birds and get evidence of possible food shortage. This information would be useful, also, in evaluating the effectiveness of the refuge.

Prior to the 1963–1964 survey, my brother and I were not well acquainted with the Sespe Sanctuary or its administration. Our experience with condors had been mainly gained in the northern portion of the species' range. Much of what I knew about the refuge had been learned through a controversy that developed in 1950 when the California Fish and Game Commission granted official permission to a zoo in San Diego to take two young condors for the purpose of attempting to propagate the species in captivity.

For thirty years no permission had been issued for the taking of condors. During this period the principle that the rare birds were not to be molested in any way had been generally accepted throughout the region. In the remote ranching country over which condors still ranged, a protective attitude toward the big birds had steadily developed with the growth of the conservation movement. This popular attitude, which was fully as effective as legal protection, was seriously damaged by the authorization to take nestling condors.

No occupied nests could be found outside the Sespe Sanctuary, and the Forest Service refused to allow the regulations of that area to be violated. Then the zoo applied for and received a permit from the California Fish and Game Commission to trap and cage a pair of adult condors. Under this new permit a rather spectacular condor-trapping project went into operation in 1952 at a location near the boundary of the refuge.

The wildlife of California is administered by the State Department of Fish and Game, which operates under the authority of the Fish and Game Commission. Traditionally the Fish and Game Department had been a central force in condor protection. Back in 1915 its Bureau of Education, Publicity and Research had operated from an office in Joseph Grinnell's Museum of Vertebrate Zoology. Harold Bryant, the head of this new bureau, was a close colleague of Grinnell. The two pioneer conservationists had worked together in the early development of wildlife protection in California. However, it was now on the recommendation of the department that the zoo was granted the permit to trap condors. Obviously, with new administrators a change had occurred in the former policies.

Carl Koford's research, although not yet published, was known to advise against the condor-trapping plan. The Forest Service had taken a firm stand in opposition, as had the University of California. Conservation groups and private individuals objected strenuously. Yet the trapping project not only received the permission of the commission but the enthusiastic recommendation of the Game Department as well.

Failing in all protests and appeals to the Fish and Game Commission, people living in the condor country took the only possible action left to them. They referred the matter to their representatives in the California Legislature. As a result, a law revoking the trapping permit was passed in 1953, to become effective on January 15, 1954.

Senator A. A. Erhart, representing San Luis Obispo County, expedited this legislation. Among the local people sending appeals to the senator was Robert E. Easton who years before had fought to establish the Sisquoc Condor Sanctuary. In response to Easton's appeal, Senator Erhart replied: "I don't know of a single action of the California Fish and Game that has raised such a furor all over the state as this permit to trap a pair of condors. Senator Ward, Senator McBride and myself will see to it that no further permits will be granted."

In the closing months of this project, special efforts were made to capture the two birds already allowed. These intensified efforts continued right up to the time that the permit expired. It remains highly noteworthy, therefore, that in a year of concerted effort, with condors regularly appearing over the baited traps, none was caught. In that period over forty baits had been put out, some of which represented the carcasses of different species from the zoo. Golden eagles coming to the food were trapped easily and were released from the traps on at least twenty occasions. Only once did a condor come to the bait. This was an immature bird that in approaching the carcass did so by shuffling forward with its body low to the ground in such a way that the snares, which had readily trapped eagles, were sprung without catching the condor.

In addition to what it revealed of conflicting human attitudes and what it demonstrated of the innate ability of condors to avoid capture, this trapping episode brought forth other important facts. Refusing as they did to come to the various baits, the condors were evidently finding an adequate supply of food elsewhere. They were clearly not suffering from hunger at any time of the year-long period over which the baiting extended. Yet the main argument on which this project had been allowed was that the condors were starving and could be saved only by being raised in captivity. This claim continued to be advanced even after the condors refused for a year to come to the food offered.

Other information that came out of this trapping venture is important for what it tells us of the condor population at that time. The Department of Fish and Game, in recommending the trapping proposition, claimed that condors were far more plentiful than the sixty estimated by Koford and that two birds taken from such an ample stock would be immaterial. *The California Farmer,* in 1952, said: "The Fish and Game Division informs us that they would actually estimate the numbers of condors in existence at more than 150."

During 1953, when trapping was attempted repeatedly on the very boundary of the Sespe Condor Sanctuary, no more than twelve birds were seen at one time. This number was seen on several occasions, although smaller gatherings were more commonly noted. Yet where twelve condors were the most seen in 1953, Eugene Percy had seen a flock of forty-two in 1945 and Carl Koford had noted one of thirty in 1946. These 1953 counts form part of the evidence indicating the decline of condors in the years shortly following Koford's research of the 1940's.

It looked as if the new condor program was failing to carry out its purpose. Koford's research was obviously being ignored in favor of propositions that were not based on sound information. After an apparent peak of abundance in the middle 1940's, and although the species now had special protection in its main nesting area, the birds were not showing up in the numbers seen a few years earlier. While published information from official sources presented a picture of condor abundance, the evidence of the reduced counts showed the condor to be in serious trouble.

It was seven years after the unsuccessful trapping venture that I first saw the Sespe Condor Sanctuary. In May of 1960 I participated in a field trip to the area conducted by the Cooper Ornithological Society. About seventy-five persons composed the party making this field trip, which was a concluding activity of the organization's annual meeting held in Los Angeles. In the group were authorities on bird preservation of national and international eminence. Escorting the tour and explaining the features of the sanctuary and the particulars of its administration were officials of Los Padres National Forest. The condor warden in charge of enforcing the regulations of the refuge was on hand to explain his work and give the current details of condor status. The National Audubon Society had official representation on the excursion, as did the California Department of Fish and Game.

Along the public road that penetrates a central portion of the Sespe Sanctuary there are different vantage points from which one may see condors. At about midforenoon the tour stopped at one of these high, open locations. Almost immediately, as binoculars were focused, a number of condors were sighted, soaring along the crest of a great rimrock about a mile away. As the birds came closer, seemingly attracted to something on a high point near by, we were told that the carcasses of five deer had been put out as bait two days before to assure the appearance of condors for our observation party.

As the birds continued to gather at the baited site, various officials explained that the taking of deer carcasses into the sanctuary as food for the condors had been a common official practice for several years. Deer killed on local highways were put in a freezer until several had been collected. The carcasses were then hauled out to the refuge.

The baited site was not only inside the sanctuary but was also within a main nesting area for which special restrictions had been established to prohibit any disturbance of the nesting condors. There were, in fact, two known condor nests within a half mile of the bait.

The officials told us that the carcasses had been taken to the site over the bulldozed roadway I later followed to reach the high peak in May of 1964. The local state game warden was assisted in the baiting project by the patrolman of the condor sanctuary, accompanied by a writer-photographer associated with a national magazine. This person, in getting material for an article on the condor, had moved about freely within the sanctuary and in the immediate area of condor nests.

Obviously such activities were considered by officials present to be in keeping with sound and proper administration of the condor refuge. Other than myself, the members and guests of the Cooper Society also seemed to regard the general situation as being highly satisfactory and commendable. The only dissatisfaction expressed came from a few of the group who felt that the bait should have been placed nearer the observation point.

As the birds flocked around the carcasses, I counted nineteen at once. Other observers claimed to have counted as many as twenty-two. This was a good number of condors to be seen in the area. Further, the condor warden claimed to know of five pairs nesting at the time inside the refuge; these were more occupied nests than Koford had found in any season of his study. If the official information was dependable, the sanctuary was functioning successfully despite the conspicuous irregularities in its administration. To have questioned at this time the baiting practice, the invasion of the sanctuary, or the artificial feeding of the condors would have appeared the rankest kind of boorishness.

I did not visit the Sespe Condor Sanctuary again until the spring of 1963 when my brother and I began our own condor study. Before doing any fieldwork inside the refuge, we had first to obtain the official permission required to enter the area. This took over three months of negotiations with the Forest Service. Even though it delayed our work, this prolonged deliberation seemed to show that the regulations were now being carefully and properly administered.

While we waited there was much to do in other parts of the condor range. We could make notes of the numbers and movements of the condors that foraged over contiguous private lands. In addition, heavy range mortality had developed on a sheep ranch about a hundred miles northwest of the sanctuary, and condors were regularly feeding on the carcasses. This offered us a daily opportunity to gather important condor information.

When the required permit was finally received, I immediately got in touch with the condor warden who was in charge of the sanctuary. He lived in Fillmore, a medium-sized town located a few miles south of the Sespe Refuge.

As specified in the regulations under which the Sespe Sanctuary was established, "One regular Forest Service patrolman shall normally be hired from March 1 through October 31 for the enforcement of the closures and fire regulations. This patrolman shall be assigned specifically to the condor area and its adjacent territory. Four months' salary of this man is financed by the Audubon Society. The remainder of his salary and other costs are financed by the Forest Service." The patrol was maintained throughout the year with the Audubon Society financing a third of the cost.

In addition to his main duty of protecting the sanctuary against trespassers, the warden was supposed to keep records of all important condor observations. This, we expected, would provide a great deal of information useful to our survey. It was with high hopes, therefore, that I first discussed with the patrolman the work we were planning to do in the refuge.

Quickly, in this first meeting and other initial observations, we found ourselves confronted with a research problem far more extensive and difficult than we had anticipated. We found that the Sespe Sanctuary had for years been operating in an almost incredible state of disorder. The irregularities I had noted in 1960 during the field trip of the Cooper Society now proved to have been mere symptoms of a prevailing breakdown of the entire condor program. We learned that tours were occasionally conducted into a particularly vital part of the closed area for purposes of having groups of people see the condors. These field trips, which violated the purpose and the official regulations of the refuge, were conducted by the condor warden.

We found an even more bizarre relationship between the condor warden and private interests operating commercially in the sanctuary and under his jurisdiction. A private grazing lease had been granted for a central part of the condor refuge under permit from the Forest Service. There were also oil-leasing arrangements that allowed occasional drilling activities. All these permitted operations were supposed to comply with specific regulations designed to prevent disturbance of the condors. A main duty of the condor warden was to administer and enforce these regulations.

We found that when not on official duty, the patrolman was employed by the owner of the grazing lease. This lessee owned and operated a business firm in the nearby town of Fillmore that sold ranch and oil-well supplies. It was also the sales agency for a type of motorcycle called a "tote-gote" that was specially designed for travel on the trails of rough mountainous country.

The use of these motor vehicles on the trails of Los Padres National Forest was prohibited in some areas, and drew general, but vigorous, opposition from some widely represented conservation groups. This type of travel in remote parts of the condor range, bringing disturbance and increased human activity, would unquestionably be adverse to condor survival.

Employed as he was by the lessee whose grazing operations he was supposed to supervise, the nature of the warden's extra employment was even more astounding. He was working as a salesman and general promoter of the trail vehicles sold by the merchant, and he was doing so in close connection with his work as condor patrolman. It was difficult to determine what, if any, separation there was between the warden's work for the local equipment dealer and his official activities as condor warden.

Actually, as we learned in later investigation, the only actual prohibition of trespass on the closed area came about through the enforcement of a local fire ordinance. Under this county regulation an extensive area of Los Padres National Forest that included the condor refuge was closed to public entry during the season of fire hazard each summer and fall. Persons found trespassing on the sanctuary during this period were prosecuted for violating the local fire ordinance rather than for breaking the federal law that applied to the refuge. Evidently only perfunctory threats or gestures were used at other seasons to enforce federal regulations.

In searching for evidence to show that any case had ever been prosecuted under the federal law prohibiting trespass on the Sespe Sanctuary, I found none. The reason given for this by various authorities of the Forest Service was that the local federal courts were prohibitively slow in processing cases brought before them, and therefore no forthright attempts were made to enforce the main regulations under which the Sespe Refuge had been established.

Taking this matter up with the office of the United States Commissioner in Santa Barbara, I could find no validity for the claim that it was either slow or unwilling in its prosecution of cases such as would involve trespass on the condor refuge. It simply appeared that no case of that kind had ever been brought before it.

Another important part of the warden's official work was in assist-
ing and supervising various groups of conservationists that came to
the sanctuary to see condors. The field trip in 1960 of the Cooper
Society was typical. In charge of the Sespe Sanctuary for years, and
officially required to observe and note all significant condor activity,
the warden could logically be regarded as being better acquainted
with the condors than any living person. He represented the Forest
Service as its main expert on the condor. He lectured on condor
preservation to groups coming to the refuge, and provided news
reporters with information on condor welfare. This wide opportunity to influence public understanding both as to the condor and
the meaning of its preservation made the warden's position one of
tremendous importance.

We soon found that the warden's knowledge of natural history
and of the condors was pitifully small. On one trip into the refuge
with the warden, my brother and I left our light pickup truck at a
point near the cattle-grazing headquarters of the Fillmore equipment dealer. This establishment is officially known as Bucksnort
Camp. From here we walked into the refuge about half a mile, up
the steep roadway that had been bulldozed through the chaparral a
few years earlier. Here, on the top of a medium-sized peak, a clearing had been made so that helicopters could land in the event of
forest fire. The old roadway continued on from this heliport for
about two miles, ending at the small meadow, or *potrero,* where
Koford had watched the lion stalking the deer back in 1946.

The purpose of our trip was to have the patrolman show us some
of the locations where Carl Koford had found condors nesting.
From the heliport the warden pointed out a big crevice in a towering rimrock about two miles away as the site of one of the historic
nests. But a photograph I had of this nest showed it to be at least a
mile from the crevice pointed out by the warden.

On this same trip, an observation of even more significance was
made. What my brother and I clearly identified as an adult turkey
vulture was identified and explained to us in detail by the condor
warden as being a young condor. This bird was in plain view, and
not more than a hundred yards overhead. A condor is more than
twice the size of a turkey vulture, and is distinctly different in its
markings and general appearance. If Eben had not been present to
witness and confirm this amazing demonstration of the patrolman's

inaccuracy as a condor observer, it would have been difficult for me to believe.

In fairness to the condor warden, the circumstances through which he happened to be in charge of the Sespe Sanctuary should be mentioned. The patrolman was a likable chap with a ready sense of humor and a sociable personality. Born and raised on a farm in the Midwest, he told us of joining the navy at the age of seventeen. He served as a cook. Discharged in California, he had worked at different jobs until the Forest Service hired him to serve in the district that included the Sespe Condor Sanctuary. In 1959, after a year of general Forest Service work, he was suddenly placed in the position of condor warden in charge of the Sespe Sanctuary.

The exact particulars of how this amazing appointment came about have not all been determined. Some would probably be impossible to document. It might be difficult to prove, for instance, whether the warden had ever seen a condor prior to taking charge of the condor program. From his own version he had no idea of becoming patrolman of the sanctuary until he was actually transferred to that position from some quite elementary work in the forest.

Obviously the warden had no special training or background for his job. Moreover, he explained that his unexpected transfer to the position in charge of the condor refuge had impressed him as being a demotion rather than a promotion. Evidently the work of managing the condor sanctuary was officially rated, both in salary and official rank, at or near the bottom of all permanent Forest Service employment. On his card the warden's official position was given as "fire prevention technician." He was probably fully qualified for this position. The card included no reference to his being the official administrator of one of the world's most significant conservation projects.

In undertaking and planning our survey, it had been expected that a great amount of information would be available from the records kept by the different condor wardens who had been in charge of the Sespe Sanctuary. These records, it was assumed, would provide basic information on such matters as numbers noted and nesting records. We had also expected to have the active help of the condor warden in the various investigations to be carried out inside the condor sanctuary.

But our first few days of investigation on the refuge had clearly demonstrated that the official records could not be considered reliable, nor could we use the help of the condor warden as we had planned. We would now have to revise the plan of the condor survey so that more fieldwork could be done in the refuge. But mainly we would have to find a way of presenting the facts about a most embarrassing and inexcusable breakdown of proper procedure in wildlife management.

The outlandish shortcomings of the condor warden and his questionable business affiliations were obviously neither more nor less than symptoms of a general weakness in the entire program of condor preservation. The incredible situation we found ourselves appraising here on the condor sanctuary could have developed only through neglect and incompetence at higher levels of administration. The underlying fault had to be in the upper echelons of the conservation movement, a fact that not only would make it extremely difficult to report—but also to correct.

Chapter VII

CONDORS on a SHEEP RANGE

ALONG WITH THE UNEXPECTED SITUATION IN the Sespe, there were other pressing developments in other sections of the condor country. I had recently received a report of five condors feeding on a calf carcass near Lemon Cove, a town on the east side of the San Joaquin Valley, near the northern limits of the condor range. This needed verification. At this time we were also attempting to determine the movement of condors that had been feeding for a period of four months on a sheep range near Kelly Truesdale's old condor nest in eastern San Luis Obispo County.

To cover as much ground as possible, my brother and I decided to work separately except in special cases. During the next week one of us would study the feeding activities of condors in San Luis Obispo County, while the other would observe the operations of a rodent-poisoning campaign on the east side of the San Joaquin. We also wanted to make an extended horseback reconnaissance of the historic Sisquoc condor territory, and to check out an old report of the shooting of two condors a few years earlier, near the town of Cuyama.

The following week I made several visits to the Navajo Ranch, a sheep range in eastern San Luis Obispo County, where fresh sheep carcasses were consistently available and condors were feeding regularly. This particular sheep range comprised about 14,000 acres. Until the late 1930's it was part of a historic 65,000-acre cattle ranch. It lay near the edge of the Carrisa Plains and a few miles north of Kelly Truesdale's old condor nest. This property is entirely grazing land, bordered on each side by two open valleys with a ridge of steeply rolling hill country in the middle. There is a scattering of medium-sized oak trees through the open grassland, with patches of low sagebrush on the rougher portions. In the early 1960's the Navajo Ranch was for the first time in at least half a century stocked with sheep instead of cattle.

The season of annual range growth in central California generally begins in winter and extends for about six months until early summer. In most operations cattle or sheep are put on the range at the beginning and taken off at the end of each growing season. Except for breeding stock, most of the animals grazed in this way go from the range direct to market or into the extensive feed lots that have increased with the intensified livestock operations.

On the more arid ranges the annual forage is quite thoroughly removed in each season's grazing. In summer and fall, or until new growth again develops, livestock would starve, and commonly does starve, on extensive areas of stock range in the foraging territory of the condors. During this period of range scarcity, great numbers of cattle and sheep are kept over on stubble fields and irrigated pastures of the local farming areas, with supplemental feeding a common practice.

Beginning in February of 1963, an estimated 10,000 sheep were trucked from other distant ranges and put out to graze on the Navajo Ranch. At this time new forage was barely started, and drought was threatening. The sheep evidently had been evacuated from ranges of even more extreme scarcity, for most were ewes in poor condition. Many came from a range in Nevada where the lambing season is later than in central California, and these ewes were lambing while being moved. Their weakened condition, combined with the effects of transportation and continued food shortage, caused an extremely high mortality.

For about four months, from the time the sheep were brought in until July when they had nearly all been removed, the pasturage remained deficient on the Navajo Ranch, and fresh carcasses were in steady supply. On one day in February, when the sheep were arriving and losses from transportation were at a peak, I counted eighty-six carcasses at different points on the range.

In March a brief storm passed through the area, with light snow and freezing temperatures. The ewes had just been sheared, and many died from exposure during this spring storm. I counted twenty-two dead ewes on one bedding ground the day after the storm passed. The suckling lambs of these ewes had not been sheared and had survived the cold. But they were not yet old enough to make it alone, and they remained, forlorn and pitiful, near their dead mothers. For the condors this area, barren of food a few months earlier, was suddenly a place of abundance.

Although these range conditions were exceptional, they came about through the normal operations of a most successful and long-established sheep enterprise. The role of sheep grazing in relation to condor survival happened to be on exhibit here in more dramatic form than usual.

As the sheep were trucked in, each flock of about a thousand ewes, many of which had lambs, was located on a certain section of the range in the custody of a herder. When all had arrived, there were six bands. The herders lived in small house trailers, each situated where the respective flock was grazed. Five of the herders were young Basques of either Spanish or French nationality. The sixth was an elderly Mexican. Operating with a small truck from a central camp, another Basque, the *campero,* or "camptender," was in general charge of the entire operation, supplying food, wine, and other needed items to the herders. None of the seven men could speak English.

The legal arrangements through which these sheepherders are brought to this country to be worked under a form of indentured servitude is an interesting variation of American freedom and democracy. Through a special provision in the immigration laws, these alien workers are imported in considerable numbers, mainly from the Basque Country on the border between France and Spain. Few have ever previously herded sheep. Bound over to western sheep-grazing interests, they are worked as sheepherders for a period of three years, after which they must return to their native country. With few exceptions we found the sheep of the condor range under the immediate care of these Basque herders, and they are probably the most common human associate of the California condor.

In the spring of 1963, near the town of Cuyama, I watched a yearling condor feed on a carcass while a young Basque herder, a boy that appeared to be no more than about sixteen years old, doctored a sick sheep some three hundred yards away.

Although the Basques were generally intelligent and cooperative, they had little special knowledge about birds. But in the tedium of their lonely work, our visits and communications about the condors were probably welcome diversions. Spanish was the only language in which we could communicate with them, and in that to a very limited extent. With a combination of signs, gestures, photographs of condors, and a few common words we were able to explain the work of our survey and get their cooperation in noting and reporting any condors they might see. While this type of information was highly variable as to reliability, some of the sheepherders became quite dependable as condor observers.

With the help of the six herders, who were well distributed over the Navajo Ranch, together with our own observations, we were able to make a thorough study of condor activity in this area during the 1963 grazing operations. From a range road that followed the central ridge, large birds on the wing at almost any point over the property could be seen. On different occasions, as condors flew along this ridge I followed them by car for distances up to six miles. I was able to watch some as they landed and fed, and see them finally rise and disappear from the feeding ground.

The number of condors and the order in which they came to feed were of particular importance as means of assessing the general status of condor food. The season of late winter and spring during which this food was available was not the time when carrion is usually most abundant. In the cattle herds of the condor range, the calving season, which runs through fall and winter, is generally over. Calving losses have been the main source of condor food in recent decades. Mortality of sheep in central California is generally low during the spring months. Mortality in the deer herds of the condor range occurs mainly in summer and fall, and would normally be at an annual low during this time. If any shortage of condor food was going to occur, it was more likely to develop during the season of our Navajo Ranch observations than at any other time of year. It seemed logical to conclude, therefore, that unless carrion was readily available elsewhere the birds would concentrate on the Navajo Ranch feeding area.

Except on the two days, over a month apart, when the sheepherders reported seeing groups of eleven and ten condors, there was no evidence of any such concentration. While my brother and I accounted for a total of nine different birds in all our observations, the largest number we saw at once was three. Identifying different birds as they appeared at different times and places, the most we accounted for in one day was six. There appeared to be no consistent use of this convenient food supply by any particular condor or number of condors. One adult bird with a distinctive gap in the feathers of one wing tip was seen on several different days, but not regularly. Evidently it was feeding elsewhere at times, though food remained abundantly available on the Navajo Ranch.

The immature condors noted on the Navajo Ranch gave further evidence that the general population was finding a sufficient food supply elsewhere during the same four-month period. Although we later estimated that there were at least twelve young condors under six years old in the total population, no more than two or possibly three different immature birds were noted on this particular feeding area.

Once, while touring the Navajo Ranch feeding area, I found a condor that was temporarily unable to gain flight. On an afternoon in March I discovered this bird as it perched on an oak stump that was located on a low point of the main ridge that traversed the range. A sheepherder's camp was located about three hundred yards from the stump. A companion was with me on this occasion; and while we watched, the herder would now and then appear near his trailer, walking about in plain sight of the perched condor.

Seen from our parked pickup at a distance of a little over a quarter of a mile, the condor appeared ill. Once, leaning forward on its perch, it stood for about a minute with its head bowed low and with its bill pointed inward. In this act it regurgitated a small chunk of material that I later found to be sheep carrion.

About an hour after it was first sighted, the condor dropped in descending flight from its perch, and disappeared in a ravine just beyond. At this, my companion and I quickly drove to a point where we could again see the big bird, which was now standing on a hillside overlooking the small canyon. As we came in sight it attempted to take flight, flapping heavily outward and downward across the canyon. Obviously having trouble in keeping airborne, the condor, as it flapped across the bottom of the ravine, reached down a few times with its feet and vigorously kicked the ground for added speed and lift.

Failing in these strenuous efforts to gain flight, the condor landed low on the opposite side of the ravine and walked up the slope to a point well above the floor of the small canyon. From this elevation it again launched into flight, this time back across the ravine. Flapping out from this higher point, it first appeared to be making a successful takeoff, but when its flight changed from flapping to soaring it began to lose elevation. Turning, it headed toward an oak tree on a nearby hillside. The condor attempted to light on one of the higher branches, only to have the fair-sized limb break at the impact, with the big bird crashing to the ground below.

Showing no ill effects from the fall, the condor again walked uphill to where it jumped with flapping wings to the top of another low stump. From there it flew a short distance downhill and perched on a stronger limb of the tree on which it had previously tried to alight. This oak was about thirty feet in height, and the bird was perched on one of the higher branches. For over two hours, until after sundown, we watched the condor as it remained perched. The big bird, obviously stranded, was evidently going to spend the night in the oak.

In this strange situation there was some question as to what the most advisable procedure might be. From all indications we could have caught this flightless condor by chasing it on foot, and there was a strong temptation to do so. Was it more advisable to leave the bird alone, or should we attempt to capture it for possible diagnosis and treatment of its malady? However, in our fieldwork, we followed a policy of leaving the condors alone as much as possible while gathering the needed data.

We had formulated this policy because we knew of the historic predilection of human beings to capture condors. This urge had been well demonstrated a decade earlier in the condor-trapping project near the Sespe Sanctuary. Our policy was designed to prevent this urge from having any influence on the activities of our survey. In keeping with this rule, I finally drove away, leaving the stranded bird on the low roost.

The condor was still perched in the oak when I reached the site about sunrise the next morning. From the sheepherder, who was camped nearby, I learned that he had seen two condors the afternoon before as they fed on a dead sheep near his camp. One of the birds had left, while the other continued to feed. This was the stranded condor we had seen. The Basque herder also informed me that, being curious to see the condor at close range, he had walked the evening before to where the stranded bird was roosting in the oak. For several minutes he had stood under the tree, while the condor remained motionless not more than twenty-five feet above.

The weather was foggy when I returned to the area, but soon the sun came out. Walking up a ridge near where the condor was still perched, I reached a point where I could examine the bird from a distance of about a hundred feet. It was an adult, with more red than orange showing in the head coloration. Once, as I moved closer, it raised its wings, and the white underwing patches showed brightly. After taking a picture of the condor, I moved away about a quarter of a mile and continued my observations. After the sun had been out for about an hour, the condor dropped from its perch in the oak to walk up the hillside a few yards. Then it suddenly took flight out across the canyon. But the big vulture was obviously still unable to gain altitude. It turned back and landed near where the short flight had started.

From this point the condor again walked uphill for about fifty yards. The sun was steadily growing warmer. After a few minutes the great bird again flapped out over the canyon. This time, after the flapping takeoff, it soared upward in rising circles, evidently flying normally. Steadily, on set wings, the condor lifted above the main ridge and at last lined out in a glide toward the southeast. To all appearances it had now recovered its normal flying ability. As the condor disappeared, I thought of how easily it might have been captured only a few minutes ago.

With the condor gone, I immediately went about gathering what evidence might remain to explain its temporary flightless condition. Various instances have been reported of condors engorging themselves to the point of being unable to fly. However, I had never found the species in any such state, and in Carl Koford's study he saw no grown condors that could not readily gain flight.

Searching the area below the bird's roost, and at the base of the stump on which it had first been perched, I found various chunks of carrion that had evidently been regurgitated. Throughout the time that the condor was watched, even as it at last soared upward in leaving the canyon, its crop was noticeably bulging. A sheep carcass near where the bird was first discovered was picked clean. Obviously the stranded vulture had eaten copiously.

From this and various other observations I have made of feeding condors, I would say that occasionally a condor may eat as much as four pounds at one feeding. In his 1953 report, Koford considered that two golden eagles and twenty-eight condors in feeding on a deer carcass ate in one day an average of about three pounds each. He also mentioned that a California condor that was kept in captivity for several years usually ate one and a half or two pounds of meat each day.

When my companion and I had first sighted this bird, a mild storm had passed over the region, followed by exceptionally calm weather. There was practically no movement of air when the stranded bird made its futile attempts to rise.

In weighing all the evidence at hand, plus other possibilities, I attributed the flightless condition of this condor to the lull in air movement coinciding with a heavy engorgement of food. Air turbulence in this region commonly subsides in late afternoon as the ground surface begins to cool. The stranded condor, in feeding copiously in late afternoon, had evidently been caught in extremely poor soaring conditions. The possibility remained, of course, that his physical strength may have been somehow impaired. Condors near death from poison have been known to recuperate amazingly, and recover the strength to fly. But this bird had obviously been well able to fly in reaching the feeding ground to gorge on the sheep carcass. Furthermore, the next morning, when at last it was again able to gain flight, it did so easily and normally only a few minutes after a previous takeoff had failed. It seemed obvious that a slight change in soaring conditions had made the difference in the condor's flying ability.

This stranded condor demonstrated the precarious, highly special-ized nature of condor flight and of the species' survival. Probably in the few minutes that this condor fed after the other condor had left, the local soaring conditions changed sufficiently to prevent a success-ful takeoff. The bird could have been caught easily and killed in this flightless condition.

The exceptional soaring ability of a condor seems to coexist with a low ability for other, more powerful and energetic forms of flight. This adaptation could explain why the flight of the condor is generally limited to an effortless glide and why these great gliders must be sure of favorable soaring conditions in cruising out from their mountain retreats. It could explain why the species has never been seen over the central, level stretches of the San Joaquin Valley or on the Channel Islands some twenty miles off the coast of Santa Barbara and Ventura counties. The proper air movement for condor flight may not be sufficiently consistent over the open sea or expansive stretches of level ground.

This dependence on favorable soaring conditions could also be the main reason why condors are characteristically unpredictable and sporadic in their foraging activities. It would be imperative that before landing to feed, the big gliders make sure that they could later take off with a load of carrion. At any rate, the more crucial aspects of condor flight have probably never been more graphically on display than in the performance of this stranded bird on the Navajo Ranch.

One day, while driving along one of the range roads on the Navajo Ranch, I saw three condors and three golden eagles about three hundred yards away, all on the ground at a sheep carcass. The eagles were in possession of the carcass, while the condors stood back a few yards.

The dead sheep was on the level floor of an open valley about half a mile wide. When I appeared, the birds all flew, with the eagles rising quickly in the opposite direction but with the condors flapping strenuously past my position toward a low hill at the edge of the valley. In reaching this hill, the condors' low, direct flight suddenly changed to soaring in rapidly rising circles. Easily, without again flapping a wing, they were soon high and gone. Obviously, air was rising over the hill, more so than on the flat where the carcass was located. Condors, whose weight is twice that of the eagles, evidently need more favorable soaring conditions to take off.

Generally condors are quick to take alarm at the approach of a car. But on the Navajo Ranch I once drove carefully toward a condor that was feeding on a dead lamb. Several turkey vultures were also at the site. As I drove very slowly in low gear toward the birds, the turkey vultures flew when I was about fifty yards away. The condor, instead of flying, walked about thirty feet, and stood watching as I stopped my pickup. It was about two minutes before the big bird, which was an adult, took flight. My purpose in approaching this condor was to measure the vulnerability of the species to shooting. I could easily have killed the bird with a shotgun.

Ordinarily condors seen leaving the Navajo Ranch would circle upward to altitudes that appeared to be from 2,000 to 3,000 feet above the ground before lining out toward some distant mountain retreat. However, on a warm bright day in June of 1963, I watched an adult condor as it rose from a carcass to practically disappear straight overhead in a steady upward spiral. Lying on my back, I watched through seven-power binoculars as the circling bird steadily rose to become a speck against the sky. In quickly changing from the binoculars to a telescope, I lost sight of the bird, and was unable to find it again. I would say that this condor, perhaps in starting an exceptionally long flight, was at least 10,000 feet, or approximately two miles, above my position when I lost it from view. It could well have been much higher.

Considering the general nature of their food, it was surprising to note a remarkable habit of cleanliness in the condors seen feeding on the Navajo Ranch. After feeding, the heads and the necks of the great scavengers would sometimes be smeared from contact with the carcass. On several occasions birds quite thoroughly and fastidiously cleaned themselves before leaving the feeding site. This was done by rubbing and wiping their heads and necks on the short green pasturage that generally covered the range. In one particularly thorough performance I watched two adult condors clean themselves for several minutes. The carcass was at the bottom of a small ravine, and after feeding the condors walked uphill to where there was a fair covering of grass. There, tilting their bodies forward and stretching their heads and necks flat and snakelike on the ground, they pushed themselves uphill while rubbing and wiping vigorously. I saw one of the condors twist its head around so that the back parts of head and neck were rubbed and wiped on the grass as the big bird pushed itself forward. I can't recall ever seeing any animal show more aptitude and enthusiasm for cleanliness than was exhibited by these two condors in their head-wiping performance.

Chapter VIII

THE HISTORIC
SISQUOC

WHILE I WAS WATCHING CONDORS ON THE
Navajo Ranch, my brother had been checking information coming
from the east side of the San Joaquin Valley, and together we made
another brief trip to the Sespe Sanctuary. We also spent four days in
the Sisquoc condor country.

The Sisquoc trip was of particular importance because it took us
through a remote section of Los Padres National Forest that at the
time was the subject of a growing controversy between the Forest
Service and various conservation groups. This argument involved
the same general territory as the historic controversy of almost thirty
years earlier, out of which had come the establishment of the
Sisquoc Condor Sanctuary. Like the earlier controversy, the present
argument had developed over a road-building project planned and
initiated by the Forest Service.

Sisquoc Canyon is the heart of what is now officially called the San Rafael Wilderness. It is bordered on its northern side by the mile-high Sierra Madre Ridge, whose unique *potreros* form one of the distinctive features of Los Padres National Forest.

Around 1960, when this area was still generally inaccessible to public motor travel, a program of development went into operation on the big ridge. The plan and design of this construction project was a typical reflection of the new philosophy that the bulldozer had brought to the condor country and that had grown in two decades to dominate Forest Service administration.

By 1963 a modern, public road was already under construction, that on completion would traverse the length of Sierra Madre Ridge and extend on to bring motorized public travel into other wilderness portions of the Sisquoc Condor Country. But a growing segment of the public, concerned about preserving this wilderness, had expressed opposition to the development program.

As it happened, for the first two days of our horseback journey into the Sisquoc, we accompanied another party of riders who were evidently being officially shown the area by the Forest Service. In addition to the ranger, who was our host, guide, and informant, the party included a member of a county board of supervisors, a bank manager, and a representative of a sportsmen's group. All were from nearby towns. This pack trip was clearly part of a public-relations program conducted by the Forest Service to promote popular support for its controversial development program on Sierra Madre Ridge.

In addition to the road construction, another main part of the development project was a practice referred to by the ranger as "brush conversion." In this work, chaparral surrounding the *potreros* that characterized the big ridge was bulldozed into great heaps, and burned. The cleared ground was planted to domestic grasses. Where the dense scrub-oak cover, about eight feet high, had been removed, the weak shale soil on which it grew was already sprouting new chaparral growth. Already chemical herbicides were in extensive use in efforts to keep the sparse stand of domestic grass from being overwhelmed by the recovery of the native shrubs.

In the geologic upheaval through which various mountains of the condor country were formed, a few areas of deep, productive soil somehow remained on the surface, but they were generally surrounded by the weak rocky material on which only the chaparral can maintain a stable growth. Surrounded by dense brush, these openings have prevailed probably since the mountains were formed. One of the highest peaks of the Sespe Condor Sanctuary is capped by a piece of this open grassland. The early Spanish settlers of the region named these natural grassland openings *potreros,* which means "fenced pastures."

The *potreros* of Sierra Madre Ridge offer a most striking and conclusive demonstration of the basic difference between brushland and grassland. In many places the surrounding chaparral rises abruptly, almost like the side of a wall, along the borders of these grass openings. Forest fires have occasionally swept over this range in the past, temporarily destroying grass and brush alike. But this has not been effective in changing the natural pattern of plant cover. As could be noted in the rocky, coarse material gouged out by the bulldozer, an abrupt difference in soil from one that is deeper and more productive to one that is coarse and sterile is the basic difference between the *potreros* on the Sierra Madre and the surrounding chaparral. The basic difference is in the soil, not in the vegetation.

As we rode through different areas of this "brush conversion," the ranger occasionally stopped to explain the particulars of the program. Partly designed to serve as a firebreak, the more extensive fields of cleared ground were explained as being mainly for the purpose of producing additional forage for livestock and deer. The cost of this work was given as around fifty dollars for each acre cleared and planted. But the continued chemical treatment of the recovering chaparral was an added expense. Recently constructed barbed-wire fences now stretched across the high ridge where previously had been the natural "fenced pastures." The ranger, speaking for the Forest Service, was evidently sincere in his enthusiastic promotion of this costly operation.

From what I had witnessed in years of acquaintance with this same practice on other ranges, I placed in my notes the following opinion of the devastation we were viewing on the Sierra Madre: "These range practices are the type now in vogue throughout the brushlands of the West. They represent a form of farming in which land naturally adapted to the growth of woody cover is cleared and planted on the assumption that it can sustain a rate of production similar to land of different and higher basic productivity."

For me, and I'm sure the same could be said for my brother, it was difficult to remain objective about what we were witnessing. Viewed from our own home territory to the north, the profile of mile-high Sierra Madre and other high points of the San Rafael Wilderness on the southern horizon had always brought us feelings of reassurance. Looking at those familiar points on the far skyline, and knowing that they hid and protected the condors of Sisquoc Canyon, always made me think of the fabulous wilderness that had covered all of central California only two or three human generations ago.

In our appraisal of this incongruous farming operation, Eben and I were mainly concerned about the effects it might have on the condors. What had already been done here to destroy the primitive nature of a historic condor retreat was serious. But as we learned from the ranger, the road-building and land-clearing operations were only part of a general plan to establish a program of mass recreation on the Sierra Madre and other wild country around the head of Sisquoc Canyon. To convert this remote area into a place of intensive human activity would be ruinous from the standpoint of condor preservation. The project could not have been conceived or formulated with consideration either for the condor or for the wilderness aspects of this mile-high stretch of condor country.

We saw no condors on this trip. The birds were obviously not frequenting Sisquoc Canyon as commonly as in former times. However, we had found condors feeding a short time before in Cuyama Valley on the north side of Sierra Madre Ridge. A few weeks earlier I had seen a yearling condor in Cuyama Valley that could well have been reared in the nearby Sisquoc area. Furthermore, condors that we watched as they disappeared from the Navajo Ranch feeding area during the previous four months generally headed southeast, and were evidently crossing Cuyama Valley in the direction of Sierra Madre Ridge and Sisquoc Canyon. The fact that condors were not seen in our rather sketchy reconnaissance of this extensive, wild area would not mean that none were there. In leaving and returning to a nest, the big birds can be extremely secretive and inconspicuous.

In this horseback excursion, camping at a Forest Service outpost in the wild Sisquoc Canyon, my brother and I had an exceptional opportunity to appraise the philosophy of National Forest administration as it related to condor preservation. This was the most primitive region of Los Padres National Forest. Since it includes the Sisquoc Condor Sanctuary and other spots of wild country, the main importance of this forest district lies in its various outstanding areas of wilderness, and one would suppose that its administration would be oriented toward the value and preservation of primitive conditions.

A popular movement to achieve permanent wilderness status for the San Rafael area was well started when our condor survey began. A main leader of this movement was Robert O. Easton, a son of the rancher-conservationist who had fought successfully in the 1930's to defend Sisquoc Canyon as condor country. A professional writer and a native of the area, the younger Easton was uniquely qualified as a leader of the new movement.

With Dick Smith, another writer-conservationist, Robert O. Easton co-authored a book on the California condor that was published in 1964. Pointing out the new threat advancing on the San Rafael back country, Smith and Easton wrote: "It involves the completion and opening for use as a public motorized throughway of an existing fire-protection road located along the Sierra Madre Ridge, the condors' ancient fly-way. This road, known as the Sierra Madre Ridge Road, lies within a few miles of the Sisquoc Condor Sanctuary and the heart of a last remaining wilderness area. Conservationists contend its further construction and opening will strike a death blow at condor and wilderness. The Forest Service contends the road is necessary for recreation and fire protection. This controversy is in effect a revival of one begun in the 1930's when the so-called Hurricane Deck Road into the upper Sisquoc River was killed by the Forest Service acting in concert with local and national conservation groups and interested individuals. At that time the easterly portion of the Sierra Madre Ridge Road, some five airline miles distant from the sanctuary, was constructed by the Forest Service with express stipulation by the Chief Forester of the United States that it and similar fire-protection roads in the vicinity of the Sisquoc Condor Sanctuary were for administrative use only, in recognition of the wildlife, archaeological treasures, and special wilderness values of the Upper Sisquoc Area. This originally firm position has gradually weakened until today's Forest Service proposes a through-way linking two state highways, via the Sierra Madre Ridge and the condor's fly-way."

Working with local forest authorities in opposing effective plans for preserving the San Rafael Wilderness was a wide representation of sportsmen's groups, as well as farming and ranching interests of the region. I had good opportunity to witness this strange collaboration. For years I had been active in a small local sportsmen's association that was affiliated with a larger organization known as the Sportsmen's Council of Central California. I had seen this larger organization captured at different times by different special interests, and used for purposes alien to the interests of the genuine sportsman. At the time of our condor survey the use of motorcycles on back-country trails of the national forests had become a national issue. Conservation groups were generally seeking to gain proper regulation of this mechanized invasion of areas previously primitive and free of such travel. In the early 1960's the vehicle interests steadily worked their way into positions of influence in the Sportsmen's Council of Central California. By 1966 they had gained dominance. Their efforts in the organization were consistently to prevent and break down restrictions on motorized travel on the trails of the public lands. Witnessing these forces gradually gain control, I would say that they could never have done so except for the active collaboration of different local Forest Service authorities.

Also joining in the movement to emasculate the San Rafael Wilderness Proposal were agricultural interests of the region, including some ranchers. This faction advocated a program of burning off the chaparral on the area proposed for wilderness. They claimed that the natural shrub cover if allowed to remain on the watershed would lower the runoff and reduce the supply of ground water in downstream areas. It was also suggested that game and livestock forage would be increased by removal of the brush. These were typical expressions of the devegetation panacea that had grown and spread in a couple of decades throughout the semiarid West. This unscientific concept had become a most effective means of procuring and rationalizing various government subsidies intended to conserve soil and water.

As an owner of cropland and stock range in this same semiarid region of California, I have observed both the immediate and long-range results of removing plant cover from the land. I have noted a consistent paradox in which early, short-term benefits often proved in later years to have been gained at the loss of basic long-range productivity. While stripping a mountainous watershed of its natural shrub growth might as an immediate effect produce more runoff and more water at lower levels of the drainage system, I would say that the ultimate effects of such denudation would result in depletion of the total supply of ground water.

Through subsidization, brush clearance has grown to become an agricultural industry. It is a significant source of income for various seed, chemical, and machinery interests. The investment of fifty dollars an acre in public funds in the "brush conversion" project on Sierra Madre Ridge is a good example of how this subsidy has worked to produce a new and dependent economic growth with strong political and bureaucratic connections. This new force, combined with the so-called "sportsmen's" organizations, the agricultural interests, and local Forest Service interests, presented a most formidable opposition to the conservationists in their fight to save the San Rafael Wilderness.

Against this opposition the conservation forces have stood their ground surprisingly well. At public hearings their witnesses have been greatly in the majority.

Our two days with the ranger and his party of observers, while not brightening the prospects of condor survival, were otherwise a most enjoyable sojourn. As a genial and entertaining host the ranger was exceptionally well qualified, and his other guests were the best of outdoor company. It was, therefore, with warm feelings of friendship that my brother and I bade the group farewell on the third morning of our reconnaissance. We were leaving for another two days of exploring the wilder, upper reaches of Sisquoc Canyon while our companions were returning to Cuyama Valley and civilization.

After our cordial parting, and as Eben and I headed our mounts up an overgrown trail that led farther into the back country, the thought remained of what might be required to convert the ranger and his guests into defenders of condor country. Already the guests had appeared to need only a little further prompting, and even the ranger had been showing promise. Perhaps another two days in the Sisquoc, beyond the realm of modern economics and away from the bulldozer, would have been sufficient.

Chapter IX

GUNS
in the FOREST

BY THE TIME OF OUR EXPLORATIONS IN THE
Sisquoc, the accumulating evidence had taken on a fairly firm
pattern. While the range of the species appeared to be much the
same as two decades ago, the number of birds so far determined
were notably below comparative counts made by Koford in the
1940's. Consistently it appeared that about twenty condors were
missing from the sixty birds estimated by Koford to be the total
population.

Various persons acquainted with the condors and their range have
expressed skepticism about the possibility of counting the entire
population accurately. This skepticism is well justified. It would be
practically impossible for all the living condors, including nestlings
and nesting adults, to appear together for a simultaneous count. It
would be almost as impossible for observers at different locations to

identify all the birds separately. The extent and general inaccessibility of the birds' range together with their natural tendency to avoid places of human activity add further difficulties.

Since only estimates are possible, the question of how many condors there are has remained fertile ground for controversy. It has been a main source of disagreement within the forces of condor preservation. Carl Koford's estimate of sixty living condors in the 1940's was considered by some authorities to be far below the actual population. As time passed, however, the accuracy of his count was steadily confirmed. After years of checking and review, I consider his estimate of sixty birds to be within ten percent of the actual number.

Koford used as a basis for his estimate the number of condors appearing at various parts of the range, and we followed his method for our 1963–1964 appraisal. Alden Miller was well acquainted with the system used in Koford's investigation. We were also exceptionally fortunate in finding unexpected opportunities to gather evidence of population status, as when numbers of the birds came consistently for months to a particular range, such as the Navajo Ranch, to feed.

As this new information was gathered, the problem of censusing the birds lost much of its previous complexity. Although absolute accuracy was impossible, evidence was readily available on which to base a firm estimate. I consider our figure of forty living condors in 1964 to have been, like Koford's sixty, within ten percent of the actual number.

Various officials of Los Padres National Forest, insisted that the total condor population was not above thirty individuals. Other authorities suggested much higher numbers. We received a few reports of condors seen in previous years in groups so large as to be far above any number for which there was corroborative evidence. According to one of these reports, the witness had counted at least 150 condors in one big flock in the early 1950's. Swainson hawks have migrated in large gatherings through the area of this reported sighting. A few persons seeing these dark hawks at a distance have mistaken them for condors. I attribute the report of 150 condors to a mistake of this kind.

One morning in 1964 I received a telephone message that forty condors were feeding on a dead sheep at a point over a hundred miles away on the east side of the San Joaquin Valley. If this account was true, it would have been proof of numbers well above any we had previous evidence for. Driving across the valley in all haste and with high hopes, I found a group of turkey vultures to be the "forty condors." It was a foggy morning, and the turkey vultures looked bigger than usual. In addition, it was early spring, and they were the first of their species to appear in this locality in their northward migration from winter quarters to the south. The observer in reporting these "condors" had been honest and sincere. He had never seen turkey vultures appear as big as these birds appeared on this foggy morning.

We also heard about condors seen in places far beyond their known range, in some cases outside California. One rancher insisted that he had seen condors swimming on a lake in the State of Utah. The birds he saw must have been pelicans.

A genial service-station operator in a town near the Sespe Condor Sanctuary told me quite confidently that the condors spent most of their daylight hours out on Santa Cruz Island, almost twenty miles off the coast from Ventura. The birds, he said, soared out to the island in early morning to feast on the carcasses of domestic goats. Each evening, he added, they returned to their roosts in the Sespe Refuge. This story of condors shuttling out to the islands across the Santa Barbara Channel was common folklore in the region of the condor sanctuary. I was never able to find that it had any factual basis. Evidently it reflected the supernatural role in nature which people often attribute to the condor. In the work of our survey this popular preference for the supernatural was a major problem in evaluating verbal information. However, I would never make light of this human tendency to exalt or exaggerate the condor; from the first time I ever saw one, the great birds have continued to impress me as something distinctly different and apart from anything else in nature. Furthermore, there is always the predilection of the condor to do what condors had previously never been known to do.

The growing evidence of condor decline called for further revision of the plan we had been following. At the beginning of our study we had reason to assume that no significant change had occurred in the condor population since Koford's counts of almost two decades ago. In what I had noted on the field trip of the Cooper Society to the Sespe Sanctuary in 1960, it seemed then that the species was holding well to its previously estimated numbers. Now, with the growing evidence of a decline, there was need for a more accurate census. Also, if the apparent loss was confirmed, more work was needed to be done in searching out the cause.

For any population to hold a generally stable level, reproduction and mortality must on the average remain equal. At the time of Koford's study it appeared that the total number of condors had remained fairly constant for at least the previous thirty years. In an estimated population of sixty individuals it was then considered that each year an average of about five young condors were being reared to flying age, with the same number of birds dying. In a situation such as this, anything that would lower the rate of reproduction by one bird a year or that would cause the death each year of one more condor than were being successfully reared would pitch the population into a serious decline.

What might have caused the loss of twenty condors in the sixteen years since Koford's report could be extremely obscure and difficult to determine. Was the decline steady and gradual, caused by some slight change in either reproduction or mortality? Or could the missing birds have been lost through some sudden disaster? Such a loss could have occurred during some particular period, with the cause no longer in operation. These and many other questions of the same nature came to mind as we continued to find fewer condors than we had expected.

As I have said before, probably the most accurate and useful index of condor status is the immature birds that normally comprise about a third of the population and generally appear in that ratio among non-nesting birds. Immatures—birds under five years of age—can be distinguished from adults by their dark head, and further classified as to age by at least three different phases of the immature plumage. In its first year after leaving the nest the young condor has white underwing markings quite similar to those of adult birds, but with a central dark spot. After this "yearling" phase the plumage is all dark. At around the fourth year the "black bird" begins to show a ring of color on the neck and the white underwing patches begin to return, with a white band developing on the upper surface of the wings. This "ringneck" stage steadily changes to the full adult plumage reached by the sixth year.

Among the condors we had so far noted, there seemed to be a

normal representation of young birds. Early in the survey Eugene Percy reported sighting a group of five immatures on his ranch. In the first few months of our own observations we had already identified three yearlings at widely separated points of the range. Two of these, and possibly all three, were different birds. This was good evidence of normal, successful reproduction at least for the previous few years.

While evaluating the condors' recent and current nesting success, we were also now giving special attention to factors causing condor mortality, particularly shooting. Practically every authority who has written about the status of the species has mentioned shooting as either the principal cause or one of the main causes of death in condors. William Leon Dawson traveled and collected extensively in the condor range during the early 1900's. Quite pointedly, and without reservation, he gave gunfire as the "first and foremost" cause of the condor's decrease at that time. In his report of 1953, Carl Koford included a summary of the major threats to condor survival. The first he gave was wanton shooting. Presenting an ample amount of supporting evidence, he included the opinion that it was not improbable at that time that at least one condor was shot each year. He mentioned seeing men on different occasions shooting at turkey vultures in areas within the range of condors.

The shooting of one or two condors a year could easily escape detection. Except for the two condor sanctuaries and certain other areas where shooting is either prohibited or strictly controlled, a condor or two might easily be shot in any of an almost unlimited variety of situations that commonly occur throughout the condor range. Only the person or persons doing the shooting would need to be aware of it. With an obvious shortage of condors, and with reproduction appearing to be normal, the main work of our survey now turned toward unearthing whatever evidence there might be of recent condor deaths.

Among those interrogated were many who were well acquainted with local hunting conditions. Consistently we found evidence of wanton shooting on the public hunting grounds of the condor range. The most interesting question seemed to be how any condors could still be cruising the traditional flyways that passed low over various ridges and peaks that were popular shooting areas.

My brother, while watching a group of foraging condors one day

during the survey, saw a condor soaring low over an area of remote
rangeland where a crew of ranch workers had just eaten lunch. One
of the workers had a 22-caliber rifle. My brother heard a shot and
saw the condor flinch, apparently hit by a bullet. With one leg
dangling loosely, the big bird, still able to keep airborne, flew on
weakly in lowering flight to disappear in a rough wooded canyon.
My brother searched the canyon but couldn't find the wounded
bird.

The suspected condor shooter was cited for attempting to take a
fully protected bird, and was brought to trial in a local court. On the
plea that the bird he shot at was a "buzzard" instead of a condor, he
was acquitted. The court paid no attention to the fact that the
turkey vulture, or "buzzard," is also protected by law in California.
In referring to condors, some people use the term "buzzard."

In fifty-six years, since 1908, this was the first and only case in
which the legal protection of the California condor was put to a test.
It seemed to reflect the contemporary status of condor protection.

The remains of two dead condors represented the final proof
needed to confirm the general evidence of condor shooting. We
learned of the first dead bird from the forest ranger, stationed in the
town of Cuyama, who was our guide and host on the horseback trip
into Sisquoc Canyon. The ranger had found the carcass hung on a
range fence a little over a mile from his ranger station. The bird had
evidently been dead about a week, and from a wound in one side he
judged it to have been shot. This occurred about 1960.

Significantly, we learned from the ranger that he made no official
record or report of this dead condor other than to inform a local
deputy sheriff verbally. He also told of receiving another report of a
second dead condor found in the same local area. He made no
investigation of this second report.

Several months after first hearing about the dead condor, my
brother and I stopped one day at the ranger's office in Cuyama to
review the matter again. A local fire official who had also examined
the dead bird joined in the discussion and offered to show us the
place where the carcass had hung, and when my brother and the fire
official drove out to the exact spot, to the amazement of all, they
unearthed the remains of the condor. Partly buried in a mound of
wind-blown soil, but surprisingly well preserved, all but the head of
the big vulture remained. The plumage was that of an adult condor,

and the carcass was taken to the Museum of Vertebrate Zoology, a confirmation, not just of a condor shooting, but also of how little there was to prevent such shooting.

From the fire official we learned that, since he was known to be acquainted with condors, he had been called upon to make positive identification of the specimen, when it was first reported, three years ago. According to him, the shooting of the condor was generally attributed to a sheepherder living nearby.

We learned that the condor had also been photographed by at least one local person and that the carcass had remained on the fence until it fell off and was partly buried by the blowing dust. That the local office of the Forest Service had apparently made no record of the illegal shooting seemed to reflect significantly the attitude of that agency toward condor protection. The California Department of Fish and Game is active in the protection and management of wildlife in Cuyama Valley and is officially responsible for the enforcement of laws protecting the condor. But from what we found, that agency remained unaware of the well-known condor that hung for months, and perhaps years, on the fence, practically within sight of the small town.

The United States Fish and Wildlife Service operates a predator control program in Cuyama Valley to protect the sheep of that area from coyotes. It seems impossible that a condor could have hung on a fence as long as this bird did in the immediate area of the trapping operations without it also being known to the personnel of this federal wildlife agency.

The California Wildlife Federation, a conservation organization with national affiliations, was also represented in the Cuyama area during the time the condor remained hanging on the fence. This large organization claims and assumes responsibility in practically all matters of wildlife management, including the preservation of endangered species. But it, too, failed to register any interest in the matter of this dead condor.

As to who might have killed the condor, there was no evidence beyond local attribution to a sheepherder. Most of the Basque sheepherders are given guns to shoot any predators that appear in the vicinity of their sheep. Among the many sheepherders we became acquainted with, none expressed prior knowledge or awareness of the laws protecting wildlife in this country.

In some instances, when first meeting a Basque herder and explaining that we were studying the condors, our explanation, not being clearly understood, was taken as meaning that we were hunting the big birds. In two situations of this kind, the herders were eager to be cooperative. They willingly offered to shoot, for our purposes, any condors they might have an opportunity to kill. Almost without exception, these alien workers expressed surprise and confusion when finally made to understand that all hawks, eagles, and vultures in California are protected by law.

Among sheep men in the American West, it is a common assumption that golden eagles prey on sheep. On rare occasions where sheep run loose without the attention of a herder, a small lamb might become the prey of a golden eagle. In the condor range sheep are grazed extensively on ranges where golden eagles are common both as migrants and as nesting residents. But in searching extensively throughout this region for whatever evidence might be available to show that eagles have ever preyed on sheep or calves, we found mostly hearsay evidence. Of the various reports we received of such predation, only about three could be considered valid. Furthermore, in the few cases that could possibly represent predation, it was highly questionable whether the animals allegedly killed were not already dead or practically dead from other causes.

Once, for instance, a few years before the condor survey, a neighbor of mine called on the telephone to report that a pair of golden eagles nesting on his ranch had been found eating a calf that was still alive. Eagles commonly feed on carrion in this region. At the time of this report contagious abortion was highly prevalent in the local cattle. In this disease the calf is born prematurely, and does not live more than a few hours. Sometimes the calf is dead at birth. Often the abortion occurs months ahead of the normal birth date, and there is some question as to whether the fetus, which may show some life, can be considered a live calf.

In the situation reported by my neighbor, the eagles had been found at the carcass of a very small calf that remained where it had recently been born and which at first appeared to be dead. However, although it had obviously been dying at birth and had never been able to rise to its feet, the calf on closer examination showed faint signs of life. According to this verbal report, there was some slight evidence that the eagles had commenced to feed on the dying calf.

To decide whether this was an act of predation, the rancher kept a particular watch for the remainder of that calving season and for years afterward. The calving operations continued as before, and with what was presumably the same pair of eagles still nesting and foraging on the same range. No further evidence was found that the birds would molest newborn calves. Another person in this rancher's place might not have waited for confirming evidence, thereby reaching a hasty conclusion that the eagles had attacked, and killed, a normal, healthy calf.

Condors and golden eagles commonly appear on the same range. Sometimes the two species are together at a feeding site. In such situations the condors could be shot as readily as the eagles by persons not knowing one species from the other.

Along with our investigation of the Cuyama incident, we learned of a somewhat similar killing in the same general region. This report came from a game warden who had seen a dead condor, two years previously, hanging from a tree at a hunting camp in Los Padres National Forest. Later I was taken to the spot by the warden. Though we searched the area carefully, we could find no evidence of remains. According to the warden, this bird had also been shot. It remained hanging even more openly than the one near Cuyama, but had received no more than casual official attention. The hunting camp was near Mill Potrero, a popular deer-hunting area not far from a Forest Service headquarters, yet no evidence could be found that the forest authorities ever became aware of the openly displayed carcass. This shooting occurred near Mount Pinos, which in deer season is a central point of condor flight and is also a roosting area. The game warden gave us written reports of deer hunters seen shooting at roosting condors in this locality, and of other dead condors that were found, evidently shot, in the territory of roosts.

The most conclusive evidence about the shooting at Mill Potrero was found several months after we first looked into the matter. Almost a year after the game warden had shown me the site, my brother and I finally were able to arrange a visit with a local Boy Scout leader who had also seen the dead condor at Mill Potrero and had taken one of the bird's wings and several additional feathers for use in his scouting work.

The scout leader lived in the town of Taft, about forty miles northward from Mill Potrero in the San Joaquin Valley. In addition to allowing us to identify the long feathers he had retrieved from the dead condor, he also gave us a description of a wound in the breast of the hanging bird that in his judgment had been made by a rifle bullet. He told us that the condor had remained hanging from the tree by a wire for an extended period in clear sight of people visiting the area. It seemed unlikely that anyone who knew the dead bird was a condor and who was aware of the laws protecting the rare birds would hang one in his camp as a hunting trophy. Some 12,000 hunters were officially reported to have crowded into this district of Los Padres National Forest the first weekend of the 1963 deer season. The sale of licenses to hunt deer increased steadily from 282,060 issued in 1946 to 448,663 sold in 1956, an increase of 59 percent. There were in addition indications of a concurrent rise in the type of illegal shooting that had long been a cause of condor mortality.

Eben and I spent considerable time during the deer seasons of 1963 and 1964, making on-the-ground observations of various typical hunting situations. Being hunters ourselves, and having considerable experience in local game-management programs, we were generally acquainted with hunting conditions throughout central California. With our ordinary hunting and camping equipment, we visited several popular hunting areas. We worked separately, to cover a good portion of the range. I spent the opening weekend of the 1963 deer season in the area of Pine Mountain, which lies in the south-central part of Los Padres National Forest. Much of this superb and popular hunting area is between 5,000 and 6,000 feet in elevation, with open pine forest at the higher levels. There are towering rock escarpments on the south-facing side of Pine Mountain. It is about twenty miles to the northeast of the Sespe Condor Sanctuary, and condors are often seen either flying over or roosting there. In his research of the 1940's Carl Koford examined the decomposed carcass of a condor that a hunter had found shot in this area. The Pine Mountain Campground serving the hunters is centrally located and equipped with tables, stoves, and toilets. Close to a state highway, and easily accessible by ordinary motor travel, it is within two hours' drive from the Los Angeles metropolitan area.

Driving toward Pine Mountain from the north on the opening day of deer season, I stopped at one of the ranger stations and obtained a campfire permit. In receiving this permit I asked the young official in charge of the station if he knew of any laws protecting hawks and eagles and other large birds in the National Forest. He replied that he didn't know of any such law.

This was a question I commonly asked of people I met while traveling about in the condor survey. It was one way of appraising the effectiveness of the condor-protection laws. Generally, as in this instance, the evidence showed an incredible ignorance of the laws protecting large raptorial birds. Often it appeared to me that condor protection was a cruel and ridiculous myth.

A few miles farther on, passing another ranger station, I stopped and talked with the attendant, who was also issuing campfire permits and in general dealing with deer hunters who were coming and going in the area. I discussed with him the highlights of the local hunting during the few hours since it had started. The official told me of a hunter who had shot an illegal spike buck and had tried to have it validated on the claim that a small lump on one of the spikes could be legally classified as a branch or point. The only deer that could be legally taken in this regular California deer season were bucks having branched antlers.

As our discussion continued, various official messages could be heard on a short-wave radio in the room. Suddenly this routine radio talk was interrupted by word that a hunter had just been shot and that a doctor and ambulance were needed. The radio voice went on to explain that the emergency would require the attention of all forest officials in the area. The shooting had occurred within the National Forest a few miles from the guard station.

I drove on into the Pine Mountain area on a narrow, Forest Service road that leads for about five miles from the state highway to the Pine Mountain Campground. Traffic was heavy, and deer hunters were numerous. The campground was crowded with many more people than the facilities could properly accommodate. I estimated that about 200 people were camped there, with others constantly coming and going.

By the time I reached the central crowded area, word of the hunting fatality in the nearby territory had passed quickly among the hunters. I was told that the victim, although walking in the open with a companion, had evidently been mistaken for a deer and fatally shot by some unknown hunter. This stimulated the already common fear of being shot, and brought forth various tales of irresponsible hunting. Generally, these stories related incidents in which different animals, including humans, were mistaken for deer and killed by dangerously unqualified hunters.

Two hunters told me about the illegal shooting of a doe near the campground. At my request they showed me the carcass lying with a bullet wound in the shoulder. The large doe had been shot early that morning, they said, before good daylight and before the legal shooting hour. A group of deer had run through an area that was already crowded with eager hunters. Regardless of the semidarkness and the illegal shooting time, a little buck and one of the does were brought down by a fusillade of shots.

Together with what deer hunting might cause in the way of condor mortality, I was also looking for what it might produce in the way of condor food. This doe lay on an open ridge where it could easily be found and eaten by condors. But at this time the area was a death trap for any large wild creature of either the air or the earth.

In two days on Pine Mountain, I was able to determine that at least four other deer had been illegally shot. Three of these were spike bucks. I was shown one of these yearling bucks by a hunter who wondered why it remained where it had been shot, near the road to the campground. This carcass was also in a favorable location to be found and eaten by condors. Examining this yearling buck, and discussing the matter with the hunter, who appeared to be of normal intelligence, I discovered that he was unaware of what constituted an illegal "spike buck."

The second morning I heard about another illegal shooting a few minutes after it happened. I met the excited witness as I was walking along the narrow road leading to the campground. According to his account, he had come upon two deer, a spike buck and a doe, which fled, one behind the other, at his approach. Just after they disappeared over a small ridge, he heard two shots. Following the animals and the sound of the shooting, he came upon a middle-aged hunter sitting on a large boulder overlooking a chaparral-covered ravine. The hunter was wearing eyeglasses of noticeable magnifying power.

At a question from the younger hunter about the shots he had just heard, the older man replied that he had just killed a buck, which, he said, lay in the chaparral a short distance below. He added that he was waiting for a companion to come and help him to gut the carcass and carry it up to the road. Walking down to where the deer lay in the short brush, the young hunter found it to be the spike he had startled a few minutes before. At word that the buck was illegal, the older hunter, with expressions of disbelief, hurried down to make his own identification. With apparent humiliation and remorse, he closely scrutinized the thin, smooth, unbranched antlers of his illegal kill. But his apparent feelings of shame and guilt had further cause for expression. As the two men were making sure that no slight branch could be found on either of the dead buck's horns, a nearby stirring in the chaparral caught their attention. Moving a few steps toward the sound, the young hunter came upon a doe, which, although unable to stand, was quite alive. Both of its front legs were broken near the body. The second bullet fired by the nearsighted hunter had evidently brought down this doe that was following the spike buck, passing through both her forelegs.

With the doe mortally wounded, there was the immediate matter of ending its agony. But which of the two hunters would fire the humane shot? Legal guilt in the killing of wildlife is almost impossible to establish unless the act is witnessed or possession of the dead animal can be proved. As yet there was no legal proof of who had shot the two deer. The doe was alive and protected by law. For either of the hunters to end its misery would be an illegal act witnessed by the other. With both men agreeing that a final shot was imperative, no move was made by either.

In frustration at this dilemma the young hunter had hurried from the scene, and I happened to be the first person he met. I realized there would now be at least four carcasses to remain as food for scavengers in this small area after the first day and a half of the deer season. Probably there had been other illegal shootings as well, to add to the supply of carrion.

While the young hunter was telling me about his experience, two deputy game wardens drove up and stopped. Aside from the regular force of state game wardens, a number of private individuals served voluntarily at various times with the California Department of Fish and Game as deputized law-enforcement officials.

Immediately the young hunter gave them a report of the illegal shooting he had just witnessed, and proposed that the officials accompany him back to the scene and at least dispatch the crippled doe. At this proposition the two wardens began a rather roundabout discussion of whether anything would be gained by their making the trip of about half a mile on foot to the scene of the shooting. The guilty hunter would probably no longer be in the area, and perhaps the crippled doe would have died. After several minutes of this talk they mentioned some other matter that required their attention, and drove away, and the young hunter, his concern for the crippled doe now well abated, walked on up the road toward the campground.

Staying overnight at the overcrowded Pine Mountain Campground, I took note of the various signs of vandalism. The evidence here was much the same as we had found in our travels throughout the public lands of the condor range. Two steel privies placed in the center of the campground were perforated with bullet holes. Camp stoves, garbage cans, and various posted signs were also damaged. Some of the signs had carried the warning that shooting in the near vicinity of the campground was prohibited by law. Here, it seemed, was a good demonstration of the "use" that for over two decades had been the administrative goal of both the Forest Service and the Department of Fish and Game.

Before this field trip, I had at times talked with different experienced hunters of the region, who spoke of Pine Mountain as one of their favorite deer-hunting areas in the 1920's and 1930's. They had all said that the increasing number of hunters had at last caused them to give the place up entirely as a hunting ground. They left the place to the crowds of newcomers for obvious reasons.

On the second day at Pine Mountain I sat in camp summarizing what I had so far observed on this opening weekend of deer season. I noted that since noon the day before, and despite a great deal of shooting, no legal deer had been reported taken in the general area. Many hunters were leaving the overcrowded hunting ground, and from their talk would never return. Evidently it was a transient population of hunters that each deer season overran the area.

A hunting ground thus nullified by overcrowding and all that goes with inexperienced and unschooled hunting had produced the situation I was appraising. In my notes I included this comment: "For this situation to prevail each deer season, and to a considerable extent at other times of the year, on the same public lands where a program of condor preservation is purported to be in operation, makes a ridiculous farce of condor preservation."

I did not see any acts of the deliberate vandalism that obviously occurs in the campgrounds where various facilities for public camping are used in target practice. Evidently it occurs at times when these areas are unoccupied by other people. Thus, the incongruity of a condor-preservation program in the midst of this year-round shooting of anything that would serve as a target is almost beyond exaggeration.

The shooting fatality in the nearby territory was of course a most unusual occurrence. However, as I learned at a later date, it was never discovered who fired the fatal shot. With as little as there was in operation to inhibit the shooting of human beings or illegal deer, there was clearly even less to prevent the shooting of condors.

Our findings showed an increase in the kind of shooting in which condors might be killed that more than matched the corresponding loss of twenty condors. Witnessing the evidence of that increase here on Pine Mountain, I marveled that any of the great soaring targets could still be sailing over the ridges of Los Padres National Forest.

Chapter X

POISON on the
CONDOR RANGE

ALTHOUGH THE EVIDENCE SEEMED TO POINT
to shooting as the cause of the apparent condor decline, we could
not yet rule out other possibilities. A single disaster could have
occurred. Moreover, right up until the final completion of our
report, we clung to the hope that the twenty missing condors would
still show up.

The loss could have occurred shortly after Koford completed his
fieldwork in 1947. The group of forty-three condors seen by Perry
Sprague on the Tejon Ranch that year was the highest number
counted at one time. Following this peak sighting, a "dark age"
seems to have occurred in condor history. A group of nineteen
condors, sighted by my brother Eben in Madera County in May of
1959, was the largest number noted and reported in the fifties. In the
official records of condor sightings on the Sespe Refuge, the group of

twenty-two sighted there in 1960 during the Cooper Society field trip appears to have been the largest gathering noted in the sanctuary in fourteen years. Koford saw a group of thirty on the Sespe in 1946, and in the year before Eugene Percy had counted the big gathering there of forty-two condors.

The question seemed to boil down to this: Did the condor decline occur mainly in the five years between 1947 and 1953 and, if so, what operated at that time to cause the loss? So far as shooting was involved, it was unquestionably a time when the wave of new hunting pressure that struck California at the end of World War II was reaching a crest and was passing through its most uninhibited stage. During this period the bulldozer was on the rampage as never before in the condor country. The roads it made enabled jeeps and other motor vehicles to bring crowds of inexperienced people with guns into places that were previously safe as condor retreats. A sudden rise in condor shooting for the five-year period following 1947 can reasonably be attributed, it seems, to the concurrent spread of mass hunting into previously inaccessible condor retreats.

As to the possibility of some particular disaster, the slaughter of a number of condors at a roost was not out of the question. During the survey, three different observers gave us details of situations in which they could easily have killed roosting condors. On these occasions the roosting birds were discovered in early morning before soaring conditions were favorable. The condors remained perched in the roosting trees even after the observers struck the base of the trees with sticks. One of these informants was hunting deer at the time. It was in the deer season of 1947 that I watched the group of fourteen condors leave their roosts in a grove of pines near Kelly Truesdale's old nest. As is their common habit, all of these birds had roosted within a small territory, and could have been shot from any point in the immediate area.

However, there were other possible causes of death to be weighed, and one in particular seemed almost as significant as wanton gunnery. With the advance of science and technology in central California, the use of poison as an agricultural tool had developed and grown apace. There are a number of accounts of dead condors found at carcasses that had been treated with poison to kill livestock predators. Carl Koford cited a report of two dead condors found in 1890 by a sheepherder near a poisoned carcass.

I doubt that any other region in the world has seen poison used so extensively, so effectively, or with so much ingenuity as in the range of the California condor. First it was used as a means of killing whatever animals might prey on sheep; later it was used to kill rodents and in some cases birds; and finally in new forms, such as insecticides and herbicides. Condors might ingest lethal amounts of toxic material in feeding on the tissues of rodents killed by poison. This is secondary poisoning. More dangerously, they might feed on carcasses that had been treated with poison, thus taking it directly in concentrated form. Or they might eat lethal baits put out for predators.

There was also the question of toxic pesticides sprayed by aircraft on vast areas of stock range over which condors foraged. In 1950 an official program of insect control was initiated in which an average of 150,000 acres of range along the west side of the San Joaquin Valley was annually sprayed with DDT. Later this chemical was found to have far-reaching lethal effects not mentioned or even known in the first several years of its widespread application. At the peak of this insecticide program a public-information leaflet on the subject carried the statement that "Many sheepmen familiar with the project, and who know it will not harm sheep, do not even bother to move them from the path of the sprayer. These men welcome the period when they are free from biting flies after the land has been sprayed. During the ten years of spraying with DDT on hundreds of thousands of acres of rangeland, there has been no known loss of any grazing animal attributed to the use of DDT spray."

Practically all of the range treated was grazed by sheep or cattle, with livestock often feeding on the pasturage at the time of the chemical applications. From what was learned later, high concentrations of the chemical could have remained in the tissues of livestock dying on these ranges and been passed on to condors or other carrion feeders, with serious accumulations of the chemical developing in the tissues of the scavengers. However, the evidence of normal reproduction in the condors seemed to rule out DDT as a direct mortality factor. Where this pesticide has been found to affect birds, its gravest effects have been in causing failure of reproduction.

From our ranching experience my brother and I were well acquainted with the use of poison. In the 1920's, when we were growing up, the bounties paid on ground squirrels and coyotes in San Luis Obispo County were important items in the local economy. With the replacement of the native grassland by a growth of alien, annual weedlike plants, and with the spread of grain farming, an infestation of ground squirrels developed.

Coyotes and golden eagles were common predators of these rodents. In the bounty program five cents was paid for each squirrel tail. I recall one haul of squirrel tails made by one of my older brothers from an eagle's nest. The two young eagles were well grown, and the parent birds had been feeding them ground squirrels. The tails of some of the rodents had not been eaten, and remained around the outer edge of the big nest to be collected and bountied. There were twenty bushy tails that would pass inspection, and my brother collected a dollar for his climb to the high nest in a big cottonwood. The land resource of the condor country was supporting a new economic enterprise.

In 1927 a general campaign of squirrel eradication was organized under official supervision in San Luis Obispo County. This program was a cooperative undertaking in which ranchers were organized into teams of squirrel poisoners that covered their respective territories thoroughly. Mounted on horseback, with sacks of treated grain hanging from each side of their saddles, a team of several riders could cover a thousand acres or more of range or cropland in a day. On some areas a thousand pounds of treated bait was distributed daily, the poisoned grain being scattered on the ground near the squirrel burrows. Strychnine, the killing agent first used, was replaced early in this campaign by a new and more effective poison known as thallium sulfate.

This organized squirrel control became an official program throughout central California. Although tremendously effective at first, by the middle 1940's it was obviously not completely eradicating the squirrels. About 1945, when ground squirrels were still common in some areas, Compound 1080, even more effective than thallium, came into general use. A colorless, odorless, and extremely toxic chemical with no known antidote, 1080 became the new killing agent in official rodent control. A deadly rodenticide, it was even more toxic to members of the canine family, such as dogs, coyotes, and foxes, and was quickly adopted for further use in official coyote control.

The effect was devastating. In 1964 it was possible to drive for hours across San Luis Obispo County without seeing a ground squirrel where the species had been extremely abundant in former years. We found this to be generally true also of areas on the east side of the San Joaquin Valley where squirrels had been abundant prior to the use of 1080. This was where in 1946 Koford observed condors feeding rather extensively on poisoned squirrels along the western foothills of the Sierra Nevada.

Amazingly, however, small scattered colonies of these squirrels still survive, probably due to lack of effort by certain landowners. But there is evidence that some populations of the rodents have developed a resistance or "bait-shyness" toward the poisoned grain. In the midst of concerted efforts to exterminate them, some remnant populations hang on as living testimonials to the almost miraculous capacity of some species to avoid complete extermination. In this capacity for survival the squirrels appear to have much in common with the condors.

The early fieldwork of our condor survey included a general appraisal of the rodent-poisoning program that Koford had investigated in 1946. Our purpose was to ascertain what, if any, changes had occurred in the supply of poisoned squirrels as condor food along the east side of the southern San Joaquin. We found the ground squirrels on this extensive range so reduced in numbers as to be no longer of any significance.

There seemed to be no proof that condors had ever been killed by secondary poisoning—feeding on the carcasses of animals that had died from poison. With poisoned squirrels no longer a significant item of condor food, there remained the question of baits put out and carcasses treated in coyote control. But with the advent of Compound 1080, the highly susceptible coyote had been more than decimated by feeding on poisoned rodents. Some coyotes may have died from feeding directly on the treated grain. The coyote is now a rare species in central California.

According to the official information we received, 1080 had not been used as the killing agent in the control of coyotes within the range of the condor. Trapping had remained the principal means of official coyote eradication. However, baits treated with strychnine had remained in official use. But this was evidently on a scale much less than when coyotes were common prior to the time of condor decline. In questioning officials working in the different poison programs, we received the universal response that no evidence had ever been found that condors or other large birds had been adversely affected by poison applied in rodent or coyote control work. It thus appeared that poison was a decreasing factor as a possible cause of death among condors.

However, just as we were ready to lay aside the question of poison, new evidence suddenly appeared that called for a far more critical investigation. In a casual conversation about the condor survey, my brother was told of a dead condor seen hanging in a barn on a ranch on the east side of the San Joaquin in northern Kern County. This report turned out to be accurate. The carcass still hung in the barn, and was taken to the Museum of Vertebrate Zoology for examination. The dead bird had first been discovered in the summer of 1960 on a stock range where 1080 poison was being applied in the annual rodent-poisoning campaign. In the opinion of local people, including the owner of the ranch, the poison put out for the rodents had killed the condor. This opinion was concurred in by the local official in charge of the poison applications. Here, then, was a dramatic contradiction of the official information we had previously gathered on the possibilities of condor poisoning.

At the Museum of Vertebrate Zoology the dead condor was carefully examined for cause of death. Although now three years old, the carcass was still intact, and showed no evidence of broken bones or other signs of having been shot. In the process of examination the head of the bird was placed in a colony of dermestid beetle larvae to clean away what fleshy tissue still remained attached to the bones. This is common museum practice in the preservation of scientific specimens. Feeding on the dry tissues of the dead condor, the dermestids quickly died. This dramatically confirmed the presence of some toxic agent, and Compound 1080, already widely considered to have killed the condor, was thus further indicted.

However, the dead beetles were tested for evidence of Compound 1080 with negative results. There was still, therefore, no physical proof of a condor ever being poisoned! The history of this dead condor threw important light on official information that we had previously assumed to be dependable. Compound 1080 could not legally be used except under official supervision. County, state, and federal authorities were all somewhat legally responsible in the use of the poison. We had been given to understand that the wildlife authorities, both state and federal, had been careful to note and investigate any evidence of protected species being killed as a side effect of 1080 use in either rodent or coyote control. Obviously, this had not been done in the case of the condor that hung for three years in the barn in northern Kern County. The death of this bird and the circumstances attending it were known among the local ranchers and to at least one supervising official of the agency in charge of the poisoning operations. But we could find no evidence that official cognizance had been taken of this significant example of condor mortality.

Another condor death now took on new and special importance. It had also occurred in the summer of 1960, and in the same neighborhood where the dead condor had hung in the barn. This bird had been found by a local rancher; it was alive, but weak and unable to fly. It appeared to be suffering from some injury, and the matter was reported to the local office of the California Department of Fish and Game. Officials of the agency went to the ranch and, according to a written statement, "identified the bird as a condor." The report further explained that the bird "had a broken wing and appeared to be injured internally as the condor had difficulty in moving. There was no indication of the bird being shot. The cuts on the wing indicated the bird had flown into a wire. The wardens took the condor to . . . a veterinarian in Bakersfield. The doctor patched up the condor, and the warden took it to the county park and put it in an enclosure. The following day the condor died and the carcass . . . was finally given to and is in the custody of . . . the Los Angeles County Museum."

Following up this case, we learned more from Kenneth E. Stager of the Los Angeles County Museum who had prepared the remains of the condor as a scientific specimen. Stager found no broken bones or other evidence that the bird had been injured. Instead, the condor was extremely emaciated, weighed only thirteen pounds, and had an abnormally enlarged liver. This pathological condition could well have been a symptom of poisoning. No tests were made as to the presence of poison in the bird's system. There was no evidence that any official attention was given this bird except to respond to the report of its discovery, deliver it to the local veterinarian, and finally to the museum. Except for a letter written in 1960 in answer to a request for information on the matter, we could find no official record of this condor death.

In October of 1963, a third condor death was discovered in this same ranching neighborhood. A rancher had found the bird dead near a cattle-feeding facility. It was then in an early stage of decomposition, with maggots working on the flesh, and it remained on the range until word of it reached my brother some three weeks later. Hearing of the matter rather incidentally in a telephone conversation, Eben immediately retrieved the now dehydrated and well-decomposed remains.

The carcass of the adult condor went to the Museum of Vertebrate Zoology to be examined and preserved along with the remains of the 1960 bird. As in the two condor deaths of three years before in this same locality, there was no evidence of injury or shooting in this third carcass. But again the stage of decomposition prevented accurate toxicological tests. It still could not be established incontestably that poison had caused the condor's death.

Though toxicological proof was lacking, the circumstantial evidence linking Compound 1080 to the three condor deaths in northern Kern County seemed almost irrefutable. None of the birds showed evidence of any other form of injury. All had been found in a single locality where Compound 1080 had been extensively applied in rodent control and at a time of year when the squirrel-poisoning campaign was in operation. Some toxic substance in one carcass had quickly killed the carrion beetle larvae that fed on it. Different ranchers closely acquainted with the circumstances in which the condors died unhesitatingly attributed the mortality to poisoned rodents eaten by the birds. This local judgment was considered to be accurate by the official in charge of the poisoning operations.

There were, however, some aspects of these three deaths that pointed toward some cause other than feeding on poisoned rodents. It seemed that whatever had killed the three condors had to be something peculiar to the area where the birds had died. The rodent-control campaign had been general throughout practically all the privately owned range over which condors foraged. There was nothing unusual about the poisoning operations in the area where the condors had died. We searched for evidence of similar condor mortality elsewhere, across extensive ranges where the species had traditionally fed on poisoned ground squirrels, but no such evidence could be found.

There were, however, reports of other dead condors found in previous years in that key area of north-central Kern County. There was also new significance, now, in the dead condor that Carl Twisselman had found on his ranch in the Temblor Mountains in 1945, and that had first brought Carl Koford to my ranch in the Red Hills. Although it was found across the San Joaquin Valley from the three condors that died in the early 1960's, the 1945 carcass was also a Kern County victim. The bird had died on a foraging range twenty-six miles from the nearest known roosting territory. The carcass showed no sign of injury, and lay near a watering site. This is suggestive in itself, since animals suffering from poison often seek water.

In a continued search for the missing evidence that might explain the exceptional condor mortality of north-central Kern County, Eben and I examined all available records and research reports having to do with poisoning operations in the condor range. At different times, also, I visited the Bakersfield office of the United States Bureau of Sport Fisheries and Wildlife, questioning and exchanging comments on the possibilities of coyote poison as a factor in condor mortality. In all these discussions we seemed to have full cooperation. Nonetheless, there was no hint on the part of any of the personnel or officials that any condor had ever been poisoned or even suspected of being poisoned.

Also, when the strong circumstantial evidence that condors had died from poison was first made public, the proposition was challenged by county, state, and federal officials in charge of wildlife control. Documentary proof, it was claimed, had not been established "to show that condors had ever been poisoned or could have been poisoned." Then, through the courtesy of the Director of the Bureau of Sport Fisheries and Wildlife in Washington, D.C., we received a report, dated March 24, 1950, originally submitted to the Washington office by the district agent in Sacramento. This official memorandum was quoted in full in our own final report.

It gave the details of how three other condors had been poisoned in 1950 at a point in the same key area of exceptional mortality. Two of the poisoned birds had recovered. The third was dead when found. Since there were two adults and an immature, a family group was considered to have been represented. The condors had fed on a coyote that had died from eating several baits treated with strychnine. The poison had been put out by a predator control agent of the federal Fish and Wildlife Service. The supervisor in charge of the poisoning operation prepared the skin of the dead condor for museum use, and it had been shipped to the agency's headquarters in Washington, D.C. In a chemical analysis, strychnine was found in the stomach tract of the dead bird.

This document opened up a hidden store of tremendously important information on the condor. Talking with the trapper who had put out the poison and had found the stricken birds, I learned further particulars of the poisoning. He was a member of a well-known family in my own area and had worked for the federal government as a coyote trapper and poisoner for several years, but had left that work in the late 1950's for other employment. According to his account of the incident, he had dragged the carcass of a sheep for a distance over the open, arid range, leaving a scent trail for coyotes to find and follow. Along this mark he had put out a number of small chunks of fat that had been impregnated with strychnine. The technique had worked. A coyote following this scent trail and picking up a number of the baits had evidently died with a high concentration of the poison in its stomach.

Condors readily feed on the carcasses of coyotes, and generally take the viscera of such carcasses first. Three or even more condors feeding on the innards of the poisoned coyote could have ingested exceptionally high amounts of the strychnine, far above anything that could be taken in by feeding on the tissues of poisoned animals. This, from all the evidence, was what had happened. The dead coyote had been picked clean by scavengers. His skeleton, in fact, was found near the poisoned condors.

The resistance to the effects of poison demonstrated by the surviving condors and their recuperative powers was almost incredible. The trapper mentioned only the two condors that had survived. He told me that when he first found them, the poisoned birds were lying front down on the ground, stiff and unable to move, but alive. They were within thirty yards of the coyote skeleton. He felt positive that one of the condors went without food for at least six days before it first ate the hamburger he fed it. Given food and water daily, one of the birds was able to fly from the area after seven days. The second bird was gone on the nineteenth day.

What I learned from the trapper had been buried by official secrecy for fifteen years, including the year and a half of our persistent questioning. It had been unearthed only by the merest coincidence. Though he gladly gave me the details about the two condors that had survived, the former trapper made no mention of the bird that had died. He told me, however, that except for his colleagues in the poisoning operations I was the first person he had discussed the incident with since it happened in 1950. There had been, he said, great apprehension within the control agency lest information about the poisoned condors spread, and there had been a firm understanding that the matter must remain confidential.

The former trapper told me he found a dead condor near a water site in the same area two years after the 1950 incident. Taking some of the longer wing feathers, he had left the decaying carcass at the site. Obviously, the federal agency had given little official attention toward avoiding further condor poisonings.

The amount of strychnine found in the stomach tract of the dead condor was referred to in the official report as "only a trace." But regardless of how much poison this bird could have taken the big vultures are prone to regurgitate under stress, and the condor was probably sick for a considerable length of time before dying. That even "a mere trace" of poison remained in the digestive tract of the dead bird suggests considerable ingestion, and its tissues might well have contained significant amounts, though these were not tested.

Further evidence of official secrecy lay in the fact that Carl Koford, then in the final stages of preparing his research report, found out nothing of the 1950 episode. He had investigated the poison operations in north-central Kern County, and his condor study was well known to various workers in the program and surely to the federal poison officials.

Koford's scrutiny of poison as a possible factor of condor mortality was inclusive. His final report pointed out that "ranchers poison coyotes and other carnivores by putting out chunks of pork containing capsules of strychnine." He remarked that it was "conceivable that occasionally a condor eats one of the baits." As to the effects of strychnine he concluded that its effects on vultures had not been tested. The true danger of poison to condors could be discovered only by experimentation on the birds, he wrote, but none could be spared for that purpose.

At any rate, official coyote-poisoning operations continued even as other dead condors were found in subsequent years in the same region. The dead condors that my brother discovered in northern Kern County in 1963 had died within about fifteen miles of the 1950 condor poisonings. The entire area is a favorite condor foraging territory. It includes a large section of sheep range where federal coyote control has been intensively practiced.

In March of 1964, at a National Wildlife Conference, at Las Vegas, Nevada, announcement was made of the two dead condors my brother had found in Kern County and of the evidence that the birds had been poisoned. Although challenging our proof, the poison authorities evidently got busy immediately out on the sheep ranges of the condor country. The official practice of putting out strychnine baits to kill coyotes in the region was at last discontinued.

However, even after its memorandum on the 1950 poisoning incident was published in the report of our survey, the Bureau of Sport Fisheries and Wildlife evidently remained impervious to the implications of its own documentation. In a new Management and Research Plan for the California condor, dated July 15, 1965, the agency stated flatly: "There seems to be no positive proof that coyote and rodent poisoning programs in the range of the condor have contributed to its decline."

In my view, poison not only is a probable cause of condor decline but has undoubtedly caused serious and inexcusable losses. At last, after a century of conjecture, toxicological proof exists that a condor has died with poison in its digestive system. Two other stricken condors, on the verge of death, had been found with the dead bird. Another dead condor was found two years later in the same area. Two condors died in 1960 and another in 1963 in the same foraging range, apparently from causes other than injury or shooting, and with poison generally implicated. Also, in January of 1966, several months after our report had been published, a condor in a weakened condition and unable to fly was captured on a ranch in Santa Barbara County. It was discovered near a calf carcass that had been treated with strychnine intended to kill predatory mammals. As in the case of the two birds that survived the 1950 poisoning in Kern County, this condor, after being kept in a zoo for several days,

apparently recovered. When released near where it had been captured, it was last seen as it flew toward a distant mountain retreat.

However, assuming that poison had caused even more than the
five deaths noted since 1950, there remained the question of whether
losses from this cause had increased since Koford's study. Our data
indicated the opposite. Poisoning operations decreased greatly after
the advent of Compound 1080 around 1945, in large measure because
this poison was so effective in eliminating coyotes and ground
squirrels. The general lowering of condor numbers thus appears to
have been caused mainly by the rise in the kind of shooting that for
a century has been the main cause of unnatural death among
condors.

Chapter XI

THE STARVATION
FALLACY

OF ALL THE POPULAR MISCONCEPTIONS ABOUT the condor, the idea that they have been suffering from a shortage of food is probably the most widely held, and the most erroneous. Although without factual basis, this assumption is in some respects reasonable. Unquestionably, carrion was abundant on the condor range in the days of the Spanish missions and big ranchos when livestock was slaughtered merely for hides, wool, and tallow, and when disease and drought operated freely to limit the great herds. Without viewing the on-the-ground facts it would also be reasonable to theorize that range losses have been greatly reduced in recent years through new range practices and veterinary facilities. The facts, however, do not support this popular belief. Since the first early buildup of domestic livestock in California, this new source of

13. *(Above)* Condor in flight at site of Kelly Truesdale's nest, as photographed by William Leon Dawson, who authenticated Truesdale's disputed condor egg. 14. *(Below)* Kelly Truesdale and his collection of birds' eggs (photographed in 1952).

15. *(Above)* The Carrisa Plain and Temblor Range beyond, seen from the area of Kelly Truesdale's old condor nest. 16. *(Below)* A Basque sheepherder, his dog and his flock.

17. Range scarcity, recently shorn sheep, a cold spring storm, all combined to produce an abundance of condor food on this sheep range in March of 1963.

18. Stranded condor on the Navajo Ranch perched where it had roosted the night before.

19. *(Left)* On Cholame Flat the author holds a calf carcass which has been picked clean by condors. 20. *(Right)* The carcass of a condor found dead, probably from poison, in 1945 near a spring in the Temblor Mountains. The bird was an adult as indicated by the bare head and the white band on the upper surface of the wings.

condor food appears to have provided an adequate supply of carrion at all times.

In the final months of our survey an exceptional supply of carcasses developed on the Cholame Ranch where my son and I had watched condors with Carl Koford back in the 1940's. Except that cattle instead of sheep were involved, the situation on the old rancho was quite similar to what had developed the previous year on the Navajo Ranch.

The big Cholame Flat was stocked with a breeding herd of at least two thousand cows when a period of spring drought and unfavorable growing conditions in 1964 brought on a condition of range shortage and starvation.

For years, even under normal forage production, this big herd had exceeded the capacity of its range. Now, as the hungry cows stripped off whatever new growth appeared, the land remained bare. The calving season on the big ranch was later than is customary on other ranches of the region and was at a peak in April and May when the forage scarcity reached a crisis. Hay of inferior quality, hauled out and scattered among the cows most of which had young calves, did little to stave off starvation. During the period from early March until late June, an estimated three hundred head died on this range. Most of the carcasses were of small calves, and generally the deaths occurred in places suitable for condors to feed. Throughout this period condor food was available in the area at all times.

As was true the previous year on the Navajo Ranch, the Cholame situation offered an exceptional opportunity to watch condors feeding and foraging. Practically all the cattle losses occurred within a four-mile radius of a central point of the big flat. Condors foraging over this territory could be kept in view from various convenient observation points.

One of the most memorable and significant of all my sightings of condors occurred while I was looking over this situation in 1964 on the Cholame Ranch. In early March I watched two condors as they fed on the carcass of a newborn calf. The big birds then performed the head-wiping activity previously noted on the Navajo Ranch. Although the ground was practically bare they rubbed and wiped themselves thoroughly. Following this, as they stood a few feet apart, one of the birds, which appeared to be exceptionally large, performed what is evidently the nuptial display of the male condor.

He spread his wings to a point about half outstretched and held slightly above the horizonal. Standing in this position with the undersurface of the great wings facing forward and with its head lowered, the strutting condor first faced the other bird, then turned slowly from side to side several times. In this display, which went on intermittently for about ten minutes, the white underwing patches could be seen flashing almost brilliantly. This performing condor reminded me somewhat of a strutting turkey gobbler as it moved about, sometimes turning its back to the other bird, which appeared to be little impressed. Although male and female condors look alike, this was evidently a mated pair with the larger, displaying bird being the male.

After this dramatic performance the two condors made a running, flapping takeoff and spiraled upward over the edge of the big flat. For ten minutes I watched them rise until the circling, ascending flight shifted, with a dip of the wings, to the set glide that probably more than any other characteristic sets the condor apart from all other living things.

However, what was of special significance in the glide of these two condors was its direction. Instead of heading northward toward Castle Mountain where the condors foraging in this area generally roosted, this pair disappeared in a southerly direction. In view of the nuptial performance it seemed reasonable to assume that this pair was about to nest. What was their destination as they headed south from the Cholame Flat out across an expansive stretch of open hill country?

The nearest nesting or roosting habitat south of the Cholame Ranch was in the area of Kelly Truesdale's old nest on the west of the Carrisa Plains. In periodic observations of this territory we found no evidence of nesting in the two years of our survey, and only once did we find any condors roosting there. In view of this I have considered it to be most probable that this pair of condors sailed on, completely across eastern San Luis Obispo County, on across Cuyama Valley, over Sierra Madre Ridge, and into some remote nesting haunt in the region of Sisquoc Canyon. This flight would cover at least sixty-five miles and require a gliding time of about two hours. Possibly the two condors were going even farther.

The Sespe Condor Sanctuary is approximately 125 miles as a condor would fly, southeast of the Cholame Flat.

The extensive range that condors may cover in foraging out from their mountain retreats was indicated in other observations on the Cholame Flat. In late April, about two months after noting the nuptial performance, I watched a group of six condors leave the big flat after feeding on a calf carcass. These birds also soared away in a southerly direction, but a yearling in the group quite obviously lacked the flying ability of the older birds. This young condor dropped behind as the others circled upward in leaving the feeding ground.

Finally one of the older birds, probably a parent of the yearling, turned back and joined the lagging immature. These two were last seen heading out together across the thirty-mile stretch of open country that lies between the Cholame Flat and the nearest mountains to the south. Evidently even young condors whose flying powers are not yet fully developed can forage at least thirty miles from a roosting retreat.

As we found on the Navajo Ranch in 1963, condors that fed on the Cholame Ranch in the spring of 1964 appeared to have food supplies elsewhere as well. Before the end of April, condors made infrequent visits to this supply of carrion. After that, for about ten days the birds were noted regularly in varying numbers up to eight in a group. However, with carrion available for over a month after this ten-day period, no more than two condors were seen thereafter on any one day. Obviously, there were other foraging areas that offered a preferable supply of carcasses. Confirming this, a group of six condors, after soaring about one day over the plentiful food supply on the Cholame Ranch, flew to another range eight miles away and fed on a lone sheep carcass.

The feeding and foraging activities of condors in the area of the big flat offered special opportunity to study the availability as well as the amount of condor food. Although the distribution of carcasses was quite even over the entire area, with few exceptions the condors fed in the fringe of ravines and small ridges that bordered the big flat on the east and west. From these slopes they appeared to gain flight with less effort than from the open flat. The condors, in taking flight from the edge of level ground, walked up a nearby slope a good distance before launching into flight. Once I watched two birds leave a carcass and walk three hundred yards over ground that was almost level, to a low knoll. From this rise they flapped to a higher point, and from there rose and left the area.

The proposition that condors require open places in which to feed was not found to be valid in our survey. Air currents seem to outweigh the factors of either terrain or ground cover in determining the availability of condor food. Extremely dense chaparral may prevent condors from reaching a carcass. But I watched five condors feed on a jack rabbit the group had dragged down an open slope and into the midst of a thicket of brush. Examining the spot later, I had to crawl on hands and knees through the brush to reach the location where the rabbit had finally been eaten.

On a cattle ranch in the foothills of the Sierra Nevada, Eben and I watched several condors feed on a carcass in the bottom of a wooded canyon. After feeding, probably because the air in the canyon was flowing upward, these birds easily gained flight. We saw them leap from the ground, with wings flapping, into a tree that stood near the carcass. Using its bill as a hook, one bird scrambled from the lower branches of a digger pine directly upward along the main trunk to a higher perch some thirty feet above. Comparing these observations to the plight of the stranded condor on the Navajo Ranch, I concluded that suitable air movement was the final requirement for condor flight, and therefore the crucial factor in availability of food. With soaring conditions favorable, I believe that condors can land and again take flight from any type of terrain or cover except dense stands of chaparral. On the other hand, without the required soaring conditions the big gliders cannot remain on the wing.

Condors rising from the edge of the big flat on the Cholame Ranch did so on some days with apparent ease, wheeling upward in effortless soaring flight after a short flapping takeoff. At other times in leaving the same feeding ground the birds flapped heavily and at length, seeming barely able to gain flight. Twice I saw condors flap laboriously for at least a mile, low across the big flat, before at last reaching an area of thermal updrafts on which they could soar and spiral aloft. In view of the wide fluctuation in soaring conditions over the Cholame Flat, it seemed probable that at times carcasses on this range would not be safely accessible to condors.

It may be that periods of unfavorable soaring conditions have caused condors to establish an unusual roosting site in a canyon near the edge of the Cholame Flat. At different times the birds have been seen using this roost in a tall pine at an elevation of about 1,500 feet. This is probably the lowest in elevation of any habitually used condor roost. Perhaps it is used only during periods of adverse soaring weather.

Recalling that condors did not appear on the Cholame prior to the early 1940's, one wonders at the ecological meaning of this change in the species' distribution. Why had condors not previously ranged this suitable foraging area? The answer to these questions can only be guessed at, but certain contemporaneous changes in the ecology of the region allow a logical guess.

On a hot afternoon in the summer of 1942, a fire that had started from the harvesting machinery on a neighboring ranch spread quickly and in a few hours swept across the big Cholame Flat. Exceptionally favorable growing weather the previous winter and spring had produced a heavy range growth. Much of this remained, even though it had been intensively grazed. The range fire raced through this dry grass with flames leaping fifteen feet high along a blazing front over two miles in width. Hundreds of cattle ran wildly ahead and then leaped back through the flames, surprisingly without harm. Hordes of grasshoppers rose in the air as the fire approached, and dropped after it passed to join the cattle on the blackened range. Obviously both the cattle and the grasshoppers were inherently qualified to cope with a grassland fire.

After the fire of 1942, the grazing pressure seemed to keep ahead of annual growth, and the area became more consistently a scene of range shortage and hunger. In good years the cattle increased to numbers that in times of drought overwhelmed the forage supply. As a result the supply of available condor food on the Cholame Ranch during the twenty-two years from 1942 to 1964 was probably greater than for any similar period since the California condor first appeared as an associate of man on the ranges of central California.

Carl Koford and I discussed the general trend of rising range mortality in 1946 as we looked over the situation on the Carrisa Plains on our visit to Kelly Truesdale's old condor nest. Koford mentioned that on the Cholame Ranch during the same period he "saw many lean cattle and horses on badly overgrazed land" and that in different trips to the area in summer he "seldom failed to find at least one fresh carcass."

Expecting the control of range disease to improve in the 1940's while the burning of carcasses increased, and veterinary services became more efficient, Koford expressed the belief that the supply of condor food was decreasing. However, the years had shown that, instead, cattle mortality in the condor range was rising. Also, of the hundreds of fresh carcasses that we examined on the condor range in the two years of 1963-1964, all but a few remained where they died, and only one, which lay within scenting range of a ranch house, had been burned.

Also, it would be a mistake to assume that such extreme range conditions existed only on the Cholame and Navajo ranches. They were exceptional only in degree and extent. To show that they also occurred elsewhere during the time of our survey, two cases may be cited in which the owners of livestock were prosecuted for allowing their cattle to starve. In both of these examples, one on the east side of the San Joaquin Valley and the other near the Sespe Condor Sanctuary, condors were feeding on the dead cattle. These were the first legal actions of the kind I had ever heard of, and the evidence through which they were brought to court by humane authorities must have been substantial. It is significant that in both cases the defendants were acquitted. The effects of range abuse were still little understood. In the local courts the starvation of range livestock was still generally regarded as an unavoidable vicissitude of ranch life.

It may appear that I am more than adequately reviewing land misuse as a cause of rising range mortality and an increase of condor food. I do so because persons not familiar with the realities of the matter have difficulty believing that such developments could occur. I myself have found it difficult at times to accept these realities even while in their midst. This was especially so one day in 1964 as I watched condors on the Cholame Flat.

Reaching the foraging area in mid-forenoon of this day in late spring, I was watching from a wooded slope above the open flat. Almost immediately a condor appeared, soaring in lowering circles over a point about half a mile out on the flat from me. It was a black bird two or three years old. This young bird was descending toward the carcass of a cow, and as it landed I was surprised to discover that two other condors, an adult and another dark-headed immature, were already on the ground, feeding. Soon after the bird landed I noticed through the telescope that the body of a small calf lay a few feet from the cow. It was this carcass that the condors were most interested in.

The adult bird was feeding on the calf while the two immatures and several turkey vultures stood nearby. The cow, lying motionless and to all appearance dead, suddenly made a struggling but helpless movement. In giving birth to the calf she had evidently become disabled and was in a semiparalyzed condition, but still alive.

To me there was nothing new or uncommon about this scene of range wretchedness and agony. With the modern ranching methods now in use on the ranges of the West, new strains of cattle were increasingly susceptible to calving trouble. Highly selective breeding, which generally ignored the cattle's natural capacity for successful reproduction, had, in a few generations produced Herefords that were inherently subject to various kinds of failure at calving time. The rapid development of this genetic weakness in range cattle was in sharp contrast to the process of natural selection as it had worked in the survival of other cattle and of condors.

Selective cattle breeding had in recent decades favored a short, compact type of beef animal with a small bone structure. Females of this type had trouble in giving birth to calves of normal size. Also, intensive breeding toward this type quickly produced a strain in which dwarfism was inherent. After this extreme was reached, it was found that the original big-framed stock was superior to the smaller type. From the one extreme the breeding program changed to an objective of maximum size at the earliest age. This resulted in large calves that at birth were commonly too large for parturition. In some cases even though the calf was delivered, it was dead and the cow was disabled. This had happened to the cow and calf I was watching.

Feeding on the calf, the adult condor was reaching through a small hole in the skin at the navel, pulling out the entrails. The two young birds stood by, evidently waiting their turn. Now and then they made threatening dashes at the turkey vultures. Once, the youngest of these immatures, in chasing and snapping at one of the smaller vultures grabbed the escaping bird by one of the large primary feathers at the end of its wing. The turkey vulture flapped and leaped about desperately, and didn't get away until the big feather gripped by the condor pulled out. At the bottom of the peck order among its own kind, this young condor seemed fully to enjoy this opportunity to bully the turkey vulture.

In judging the availability of condor food, there was the question of whether the big vultures could open the tough hides of grown cattle. We were never able to settle this question. Only in rare instances were condors noted feeding on large carcasses, and in these cases there was no evidence that the birds had themselves opened the hide.

Perhaps our failure to resolve this question was due to the condors having at all times a choice of small carcasses such as calves, sheep, or deer. Feeding on these smaller animals, the big scavengers would generally consume the innards first, pulling the food out through the anal opening or a hole made at the navel or elsewhere in the abdomen. Where all the edible parts on a carcass were eaten, the carrion was usually pulled out through a single opening, with the hide at last turned completely inside out and the bare skeleton remaining attached.

Watching the feeding condors from my strategic observation point, I could observe other activities on the big flat. A county highway passed through the center of the area, approximately two hundred yards beyond the feeding birds. Without moving the telescope I could see both the condors and the passing traffic. Sixteen different cars and trucks passed in the five hours that the birds remained at the feeding site. The condors appeared to give little, if any, heed to the various vehicles. There was no sign that the people traveling by knew that three California condors were standing in open view not more than two hundred yards from the road.

Later, however, I learned that these condors were far more watchful and apprehensive than they appeared. When I returned the next day, the birds were again on the ground at the same carcass. To check their seeming lack of concern toward vehicles, I first drove by the location as in normal travel. The big birds gave no sign of concern. Going on about two miles and turning back, in passing the location again I gradually slowed to a stop. Immediately the condors scrambled into flight.

Shooting from cars has been a common practice for decades along the remote public roads of the condor range. In this type of shooting, which may be directed toward any form of wildlife, various species of birds have come to recognize the danger of a car that stops as it passes within shooting range. Ravens in the condor country are especially notable for their intelligent response to this sign of danger.

The wind was brisk on the day that I watched the three condors. This was probably an important factor in the birds choosing to feed at such an unusual distance out in the open flat. As they rose from the area in late afteroon, they did so easily on the strong breeze. With the adult towering upward first and lining out, the two immatures quickly followed. Through the telescope I watched them fade from view, toward the north, one behind the other, in the direction of Castle Mountain.

As the gliding condors disappeared, and with my telescope still focused on the distant mountain peak, I was especially struck by the remoteness of that remnant piece of back country. The farthest removed from human activity of any spot in the region, it stood in dramatic contrast to the scene I had previously been watching. With this paradox in mind, as I finished a few last notes I added the question: "On what is the condor most dependent—undefiled wilderness, or wretchedness and travail on the grazing lands?" Leaving the big flat, I stopped where two ranch hands were scattering hay among the starving cattle, and told them of the dying cow.

I doubt that deer ever inhabited the open, rolling grasslands of eastern San Luis Obispo in aboriginal times. My father was an eager hunter, but at the time of his death in 1935 he had never seen a deer in McMillan Canyon. Until about 1940 the deer of the condor country were restricted to wooded range. About that time, however, they began to spread into the more open areas, including McMillan Canyon, and to increase rapidly.

In the summer of 1964, driving for a distance of three miles along the edge of an extensive alfalfa field a few miles south of Shandon, I counted as many as a hundred deer feeding on the alfalfa, where, before the early forties, there had been no deer. This sudden spread and increase of deer was general throughout the condor range.

Kelly Truesdale, living for a few years just before 1920 on his homestead in the Red Hills, never saw a deer or a condor in that territory. On my ranch in the same area I first saw deer in the early 1940's. In a few years they were common, in some situations causing considerable damage to grain crops. Following this rapid buildup, die-offs from disease and parasitism began to be noted. Around 1950, when deer were dying and the carcasses were common on the local range, I saw condors in the Red Hills for the first time. Deer are a preferred condor food.

But this appearance of foraging condors in a new territory should not be mistaken as an indication of food shortage elsewhere. The proliferation of deer was general, and what seemed most likely was that the condors were now ranging a new foraging territory made suitable for the first time by a new supply of carrion.

In my judgment, this increase of deer was a result of four main factors: General decimation and in some areas extermination of the coyote had removed predation as a natural control of the deer. Extensive new development of irrigated crops, mainly alfalfa, together with the growth on arid croplands of nutritious alien summer weeds offered succulent green forage to deer during the dry seasons of summer and fall. New economic conditions had made venison no longer a factor of local human subsistence. Increasing game-law enforcement allowed only male deer to be hunted. As a result, deer now multiplied unchecked.

I have previously pointed out how poison destroyed the coyote populations of central California. The Red Hills were a center of coyote abundance up to the 1930's when thallium sulfate as a rodent poison reached full use. Its secondary effects on animals feeding on the poisoned rodents were decimating. In the 1940's the more drastic effects of the new Compound 1080 annihilated the coyote. Our daughter was born in 1939 and grew up on the ranch in the Red Hills. She was fifteen years old before hearing for the first time the howl of a coyote.

Deer, especially young fawns or individuals weakened by hunger, disease, or parasitism, when in open territory away from escape cover are vulnerable to coyotes. During the time of our survey dogs were catching and killing deer in the Shandon area. A local rancher reported seeing two coyotes chasing a two-year-old buck deer in the fall of 1963. In 1959, during a time of heavy deer die-off, a rancher in the area of Castle Mountain saw a coyote attempt to catch a fawn.

In natural deer habitat of rough terrain and woody cover, this predation would probably apply only to numbers in excess of optimum range capacity. In early times, before there was any effective control of coyotes, deer were abundant on the wooded ranges of the condor country. I believe, however, that under natural conditions the high coyote population on the rich open grasslands was a main factor causing those areas to be untenable for deer.

The absence of coyotes has contributed to the supply of condor food in various ways. Free of this natural control, the excessive deer populations that developed have been limited by various forms of die-off in which the carcasses remain on the range, untouched by predators, in many cases available as condor food.

During the 1950's a group of nonbreeding condors ranged each summer for a hundred miles northward from the Cholame Ranch. This annual drift, like the appearance of condors on the big ranch itself, was also a new development. It repeatedly occurred when the heavy deer populations that had developed in the same region, were suffering die-offs.

The deer situation in the condor range from the early 1940's to the time of our survey resembled closely the ecology of range livestock in the same region for the same period. The results of overpopulation could be observed in the periodic deer die-offs, as had been found in the exceptional sheep and cattle losses on the Navajo and Cholame ranches in the two years of our fieldwork. Incredibly, however, the deer losses were even more extreme and extensive. As I said of cattle carcasses on the Cholame Ranch, I would say that more dead deer were available as condor food during the two decades prior to and including the time of our survey than had ever previously occurred in the history of either deer or condors.

The widely accepted notion that condors were starving in the midst of this abundant supply of carrion was difficult to explain. The facts of increasing deer and the correlated range die-offs were publicly disseminated by the California Department of Fish and Game. Yet the same wildlife agency thought condors were starving.

The Game Management Supervisor of the Department of Fish and Game in Los Angeles wrote me: "I strongly suspect that food is the main limiting factor of the California condor. We no longer have bands of antelope or herds of deer roaming the valleys in the counties of Los Angles and Kern. No longer do large herds of elk inhabit the San Joaquin Valley. These animals in turn probably supplied enough food as fresh meat and carrion to support many other animals which in turn would eventually die. It is safe to say that the condor has considerably less food now than in previous days. Deer, elk and antelope were generally replaced by livestock. For a period of time, it is my understanding that tallow and hides were the only portion of cattle utilized and the carcasses were not utilized by man. Again, there was an available food supply for condors.

"I believe condors are having a difficult time obtaining food now. Most of the deer are confined to brushy slopes. The death of a deer may not provide food for practical purposes for condors in many instances because the location of the dead deer may be such that the condor may not be able to attain flight. This, then, leads to speculation that if adult condors are having a difficult time providing themselves with food, the chances of young, dependent birds are even slimmer towards securing adequate food. . . .

"Successful maintenance of the California Condor population in the wild state would seem to me to depend on creating an environment similar to that which the condor enjoyed many years ago. Without a food supply that caters to the flight limitations of the condor, I question there are any management efforts that will be successful in maintaining a condor population in the wild state. It appears to me that the only salvation for the condor in the wild is an artificial feeding program."

This fallacious assumption that the condors are starving has been seriously damaging. It has diverted attention and concern from the real facts of condor welfare, and it has been exploited in various ways to bring new adversity to the species. This does not mean, of course, that food, always the basic requirement for survival, could not become scarce for the condors or that it should not be carefully and continually appraised. If and when real evidence is found that the species is threatened with food shortage, action should certainly be taken to assure an adequate supply.

Chapter XII

MORE TROUBLE
in the REFUGE

THROUGHOUT OUR INVESTIGATIONS IN OUT-lying areas of the condor range, trips to the Sespe Sanctuary continued to be a main part of our fieldwork. To cover as much area as possible, I worked in and around the sanctuary while my brother studied the region bordering the southern San Joaquin Valley. However, in order to evaluate certain situations more critically, we occasionally worked together.

In search of nesting condors, by the second summer of the study I had spent at least one day within view of every section of the Sespe Sanctuary. On foot, with binoculars, telescope, notebook, camera, a light sleeping bag, food to last two days, and a gallon jug of water, I would hike to some strategic point in the refuge and watch for birds.

These days were all memorable experiences. Although signs of illegal infringements were common in the more accessible parts of the sanctuary, its central portions were places of seclusion, away from human disturbance. I have never seen a landscape anywhere that could match this last stronghold of the condor in the picturesque profusion of its towering peaks and rimrocks and its crooked, cliff-walled canyons.

Staying overnight so as not to miss some early or late condor activity, I had a chance to observe other wildlife in the area. Mountain lions, like the condors, seemed to find the refuge a favorite retreat. I often saw lion tracks on the trails of the closed territory. The big cats are becoming extremely rare in central California, and their tracks somehow enhanced the intrinsic wildness of the remote areas of the refuge. Generally I found evidence of nesting condors where I saw the lion tracks, in places where both were as far as either a condor or a lion could get from the reach of man.

In some areas where nesting was indicated, I spent several days watching from a distance, taking no chance of causing the failure of a nest. We considered adult birds, singly or in pairs, seen to be frequenting particular areas of nesting habitat during the summer and fall as being the only nesting evidence we could obtain. This, of course, was subject to further confirmation in the appearance of immature birds.

In fact, as the survey progressed, the more it became obvious that the best indications of successful reproduction are the immature condors themselves. At least three age classes can be distinguished in the field. Active nests are no assurance of rearing success. Our main purpose in noting evidence of nesting in the refuge was to appraise the use of the area as breeding habitat. On both summers of the survey, we found satisfactory evidence that the Sespe Sanctuary continued to function as the main nesting center of the condors.

Only once did we examine a nest cave—and this was only after we were sure that it was not in use at the time and because we needed to get evidence concerning previous human disturbance at the site. The invasion of this nesting territory in an illegal but officially conducted photography project turned out to be one of the more important findings of our condor survey. It came as a final episode in a steady sequence of irregularities in the Sespe Sanctuary.

Our early discoveries that the administration of the condor refuge was in a general state of disorder were soon followed by further confirming evidence. The problem proved even more serious and deeply rooted than we had at first assumed. Expecting to find that the condor patrolman was highly exceptional in his shortcomings, we interviewed other Forest Service officials who were in direct authority over the administration of the Sespe Sanctuary and over the work of the warden.

The welfare of the condor as an official responsibility seemed to have been casually abandoned by the Forest Service. Questioning some officials, I was told that the management and protection of the wildlife on the National Forest was not their responsibility but that of the California Department of Fish and Game.

This was technically true. Around 1940, when competition for growth and power was developing among the resource management agencies, authority and responsibility in matters of wildlife protection on the national forests of California had passed almost exclusively to the jurisdiction of the California Department of Fish and Game. Prior to this separation of functions, some of the most effective officials working in the enforcement of game laws and wildlife conservation were the rangers of the national forests. However, at the time of our survey it seemed that the only law that greatly concerned forest officials was that pertaining to the prevention and control of forest fires.

This removal from the rangers of traditional responsibility and authority in matters of general law enforcement had caused a profound change in their traditional role as protectors of the forest and of the wildlife. In my view this has been the major cause of the general lawlessness that we found had developed in recent years on the national forests. The loss of this official protection could well have caused the difference between the condor population found by Carl Koford in the 1940's and the lowered numbers we were counting in the early 1960's.

One of the most striking aspects of the lack of knowledge or interest about the condor found among Forest Service officials and personnel was the common assumption that among flying condors the immatures were smaller than older birds. Actually, raptorial birds generally have their full growth when first on the wing, and the smallest flying condor would have a wingspread of over eight feet. Commonly, when we received official information about condors, the age of the birds was specified. Questioning our informants as to how they distinguished between young and old condors, we were amazed when told that the bird's size was their only criterion of age. When first told of young condors seen soaring overhead that were "just out of the nest" with "wingspreads of no more than four feet," it seemed that a joke was intended. However, we quickly found the wingspread fallacy to be a matter of sincere and firm belief.

Occasionally we found a Forest Service employee who did know condors. One official working at the central office of the Los Padres National Forest in Santa Barbara was a veteran ranger and the packer who had taken Carl Koford into the Sisquoc Condor Sanctuary on horseback at the time of the previous condor study. We also found different persons in charge of the various fire lookouts who were interested in the condor program and thoroughly experienced in their work. These few veteran workers were accurate and dedicated condor observers. But the great majority of persons of all rank working in the administration of Los Padres National Forest knew practically nothing about the California condor or the program for its preservation. The condor warden, who had amazed us with his identification of a turkey vulture as a condor, was the official expert in all matters of condor management on Los Padres National Forest.

This general lack of knowledge about the condor within the administration of Los Padres National Forest somewhat absolved the condor warden from the fault that might otherwise have been his. As we were finding in the entire spectrum of condor preservation, the basic weakness of the program could be traced to the higher echelons of bureaucratic administration. And even there it was only a symptom of a more profound weakness. Its real origins lay in the human society that was reflected in the bureaucracy.

This hidden fault was typically confirmed early in our survey in a conversation I had with a young state game warden. I had met with this young wildlife official to enlist his cooperation and that of several other local game wardens of whom he was the captain. The region under his general jurisdiction included a main, central foraging ground of the condor where enforcement of the laws protecting non-game wildlife was of particular importance in the species' welfare.

Meeting this warden for the first time, I was favorably impressed by his appearance and demeanor. Such superficial indications can, of course, be misleading. But as material out of which to build a strong and effective program of condor protection, this young official appeared to have the natural qualifications in pronounced form. He told me of growing up in the town of Fillmore, near the Sespe Condor Sanctuary, and of choosing as his life work the career of a game warden.

But this warden, too, knew practically nothing about the condor. I had with me a copy of Koford's 1953 report, which I referred to and which I learned he had never heard of. Significantly, however, he was eager to get hold of a copy. I mentioned the historic condor nest discovered in 1950 in the big tree on the west slope of the Sierra Nevada and I brought up the matter of the ailing condor that had died in a Bakersfield zoo in 1960. The locations of these two occurrences and of the other recent Kern County condor deaths were within the area of the warden's jurisdiction. He had no knowledge of any of them. Obviously, the California condor had been given no consideration by the California Department of Fish and Game in the training and general orientation of this outstanding game warden.

Throughout our conversation the warden had been frank and open in revealing his lack of acquaintance with the condor. Finally, as I was leaving, and apparently to be sure of having it understood, he mentioned this shortcoming. "Mr. McMillan," he remarked, "this may be something of a disgrace, but I really can't say that I would know a condor if I were to see one overhead in ordinary flight."

My reply may have surprised and perhaps confused the young official. "There's no disgrace in what you have just said," I assured him. "In fact your statement marks you as being qualified for the work of condor preservation in ways far more important than just being able to identify a flying condor." I wanted this young warden to understand that in having the ability to know that he knew very little about the condor and to say so frankly, he was demonstrating the plain intelligence and simple integrity on which condor preservation had been founded and on which it remained dependent.

A few months after our first observations on the Sespe Sanctuary, the magnitude of its bizarre mismanagement was acutely demonstrated. In accord with the official management plan for the refuge, an Advisory Committee had been established in 1948, with its stipulated purpose to "advise the Forest Supervisor in policy matters pertaining to the management of the Sespe Wildlife Area." (The latter was the official title of the refuge, and a sad misnomer because it confused the condor with game species and nonprotected wildlife.) The committee was officially composed of the President of the National Audubon Society, the Director of the Museum of Vertebrate Zoology, and the Assistant Regional Forester in charge of Wildlife Management of the Forest Service. In the fall of 1963, when our survey was well along, this committee held a meeting in San Francisco, its first in fifteen years!

At this meeting, which was attended by two of the higher officials of the Forest Service, a letter of protest received by the President of the National Audubon Society from one of that organization's California branches was read. Dated December 5, 1963, the letter was in protest of irregularities it claimed were being knowingly allowed by the Forest Service in the management of the Sespe Condor Sanctuary. It claimed that the trail corridor traversing the refuge was being used "by a salesman to demonstrate tote-gotes." As something "more incredible still," it asserted that the salesman was the Forest Service official in charge of the condor sanctuary. It further alleged that the same official was employed on weekends by the local business firm that sold the trail vehicles and had "other business interests in the area, including a grazing allotment on the sanctuary which the ranger, when wearing his ranger hat, has the duty of supervising."

Confronted with this specific protest, the Forest Service officials, with obvious show of concern and with outspoken condemnation of the alleged activities, assured all present that an investigation would be made and remedial action taken if the charge was confirmed. These two higher officials were in authority at the state and regional level over the administration of the condor sanctuary and of all wildlife in the National Forest. Their obvious lack of knowledge about the conduct of the condor program seemed no less incredible than the warden's bizarre business affiliations.

About a month later the Forest Service reported that the Supervisor of Los Padres National Forest had investigated the case and found only a partial foundation for the critical letter. It specified: "The Sespe Wildlife Area Patrolman does not issue permits to enter the wildlife area without prior approval of the District Ranger in each case." In further denial it included: "The patrolman has never sold tote-gotes, nor has he demonstrated their use for sale purposes within the Sanctuary." The report added, however, that in March of 1963, the patrolman had been officially instructed "to discontinue the use of a tote-gote within the area and did so." It also stated that the patrolman had informed the head office that he had severed connections with the local business firm.

Evidently, from this report, the Forest Service was no more capable of objectively and accurately appraising its own faults than were the official poison dispensers of the Bureau of Sport Fisheries and Wildlife. As the outlandish evidence about the management of the condor refuge accumulated, the problems of appraising and reporting its details increased. Nonprofessionals in wildlife management, Eben and I were even less prepared to act as experts on human behavior. Even an expert on the subject would have found it a difficult and unsavory task to classify and report the facts of human behavior that continually confronted us in appraising the administration and management of the Sespe Condor Sanctuary.

We did know that when confronted with a need for correction in matters within their administration, public agencies will take remedial action even while refusing to acknowledge the facts. Having assumed that some action of this kind would surely be taken to remedy the problem on the condor refuge, we were even more astonished to read a few months later in *The Santa Barbara News-Press* that the warden still maintained his questionable business affiliations. The newspaper item read in part as follows: "William Hansen, supervisor of Los Padres National Forest, said yesterday he would immediately investigate reports that an Ojai District patrolman is continuing to sell and demonstrate 'tote-gotes' for a Fillmore firm, after being ordered nine months ago to sever his connections with the company."

The account went on to give the details of a telephone conversation between a news reporter and the Fillmore businessman with whom the condor patrolman was evidently still associated. Evidently the merchant was not aware that he was talking to a reporter. As quoted in the news item, he freely explained that the condor warden had worked for his company, selling the trail vehicles on his time off, and had been criticized for this by the Forest Service. With the reporter indicating an interest in buying a tote-gote through the warden, the merchant was quoted as saying, "We'll try to use him, but at the same time will protect him." He informed the reporter that the patrolman had one of the vehicles at his house "and will demonstrate it for you; or I can get it and have it here at the store."

This news indicated among other things that the situation in question had been known for almost a year by the office in charge of Los Padres National Forest and the Sespe Sanctuary.

But making these bureaucratic deficiencies all the more incredible, yet all the more undeniable, was an incident in the condor refuge that had occurred some two months before the account of the patrolman's tote-gote operations appeared in the Santa Barbara newspaper. More astonishing still, it happened after the Forest Service had purportedly investigated the warden's activities and corrected him in matters of his official work.

Early on the morning of February 18, 1964, intending to spend two days in census work, I drove to the end of the public road in the condor refuge. Leaving my pickup near Bucksnort Camp, I began hiking up the old bulldozed roadway to the heliport where the condor patrolman had amazed us with his identification of a turkey vulture several months before.

Immediately I noted the fresh tracks of a vehicle that evidently was ahead of me on this seldom-used roadway. Reaching the heliport I noted a herd of eleven deer in a nearby opening; at the sight of me they bounded away into the chaparral. Except for the tracks of the vehicle, I saw no other evidence of recent human activity. Although it was still early, the grazing deer were evidence that the vehicle had passed through the area a considerable time before my arrival.

To investigate the meaning of the car tracks, I walked on about a mile and a half up the steep and somewhat overgrown course of the old firebreak and found a small four-wheel-drive truck parked at its end. It was a Forest Service truck ordinarily used to transport a trail crew working in another area and using Bucksnort Camp as a base of operations.

Several cattle were grazing here on the small *potrero* where the lion stalked the deer back in 1946. The parked vehicle was within about three-eighths of a mile of two condor nests that Koford had found in the 1940's. The two nest sites were inside a section of the sanctuary in which nesting condors were given special protection from disturbance. Human footprints on an old trail entered dense cover at the edge of the *potrero* and led on in the direction of one of the nearby condor nests. Parked in the immediate vicinity of two known condor nests, over two miles inside the sanctuary, the truck and those who had driven it almost certainly had violated refuge regulations. It would be a requirement of our work to explain this evidence that, even as it stood in plain sight, was difficult to believe.

Deliberating for a moment on how to approach this problem, I took from my pocket the official permit required of persons entering the closed area, and read its list of specifications. I had agreed to the following commitments: "It is understood that I have or will secure knowledge of the Federal, State and County laws or regulations governing the use of the National Forest and agree to strictly observe them. To avoid any disturbance or molestation of condors or condor nests. Not to knowingly approach within one-half mile of nesting condors. To report the presence of any unauthorized persons in the Condor Refuge."

The requirements of my official permit as well as my work left me no real choice. I took a few pictures of the truck and its surroundings, then hurried back to my pickup and took the road to Fillmore. Arriving there at noon, I telephoned the Ojai office of the Forest Service that had authority over the condor refuge. Learning that no officials were on hand there to deal with my report, I called the office of the Supervisor of Los Padres National Forest in Santa Barbara.

Through this head office my call was transferred back to the local District Ranger at Ojai to whom I reported the evidence of trespass on the condor sanctuary. The ranger assured me that no permission had been issued by his office that would allow a vehicle to be inside the refuge. He explained that the condor patrolman was not supposed to be driving over the old fire road and that for any vehicle to be where I had found the truck would be a violation of the sanctuary regulations.

I then requested that the ranger come or send a representative of his office to be with me back at Bucksnort Camp when the truck I had found came out of the refuge. I explained that I wanted to have the facts about the trespass brought out in fair and open discussion in front of an official witness. The ranger, who could not get away himself, agreed to send another official to represent his office, and assured me that this official would join me in an hour and a half at the spot where the truck in question would have to return to the public corridor.

Returning to the refuge, I met the condor patrolman in his regular pickup before I reached Bucksnort Camp. Another man was with him. Stopping as we met on the narrow road, we exchanged greetings, and the warden introduced his companion as a photographer who was in the area getting pictures of condors. They explained that during that morning and the day before they had seen in the Bucksnort area condors that had offered good photographic opportunities. They mentioned getting pictures of a condor perched in a tree at close range. Thinking of the truck I had discovered in the refuge, I asked the photographer if he had a permit to enter the closed area. The warden then quickly explained that they had not entered the refuge but had remained on the public corridor.

I told the patrolman that I had been in the Bucksnort area that morning and had found evidence that someone was in the refuge. The warden then admitted that some pictures had been taken from the heliport on the low peak near Bucksnort, inside the refuge. I then told of finding the four-wheel-drive truck a mile and a half or more beyond the heliport. To explain this the patrolman said that he had left the photographer at the heliport and had driven on in a search for trespassers, leaving the truck where I had found it.

At this point I explained to the warden, with whom I had remained in friendly and cordial contact, that I had planned to discuss the question with whoever had driven the truck into the closed area and that I had made arrangements for another ranger to be present at the talk. Both the patrolman and the photographer agreed to wait with me at a nearby forest guard station until the official arrived.

As we talked casually about other matters, it turned out that the photographer was a public-relations agent for a national produce company. It was mentioned that cattle had been photographed on the range in the Bucksnort area, and at this I recalled noting several cows and calves grazing near the parked truck. These were the only cattle I had seen.

Soon the official we were waiting for arrived. This ranger's attitude was belligerent, and immediately he and the condor patrolman joined in an obvious effort to discourage me from going into the matter as I had proposed to do. It seemed that I had violated protocol. I should have taken the matter up with the Ojai office before making a report to the higher authority in Santa Barbara. The local official could have explained everything about the photography operations, he said. The project had official approval and had been cleared and arranged months before. My action was referred to as that of a "buck private going over his superior officer to report something to a general."

I replied that I might be mistaken, but that if so I would simply like to see the official permit that allowed the photographer to be in the condor sanctuary. Both rangers informed me that there was no need of such official permission so long as the person entering the refuge was accompanied by a Forest Service official. This, I well knew, was not correct.

I then explained to the two rangers that I had assumed the task of ascertaining the facts about the condor and its welfare and they could either give me the facts about the photographic expedition or I would have to dig out the information as best I could. This elicited no cooperation, so I left the group.

The next afternoon I was back in the Bucksnort area with the Assistant Supervisor of Los Padres National Forest and the Assistant Ranger of the Ojai District, to review the evidence of the human activities here the day before. In Santa Barbara that morning I had presented my problem to the Forest Supervisor and had been successful in arranging an immediate on-the-ground review of the evidence. I learned that no permit had been issued for the photographic operations, and by all appearances the project had been arranged and carried out without the knowledge of any official other than the condor warden and his colleague who had come to join us in discussing the matter the day before.

Walking up the steep, bulldozed track through the chaparral, I first pointed out to the two officials that only two sets of tire tracks existed, showing that a single trip had been made up and back. This was important, since the warden claimed that he had first driven the photographer to the heliport in his regular truck, then returned to Bucksnort Camp and taken a different four-wheel-drive truck back over the route and on to the far peak. This would have left four sets of tracks in the old roadway.

At the heliport the photographer was supposed to have remained several hours taking pictures and putting up a blind, so I asked the two officials to scrutinize the area for evidence that any such activity had occurred. My own tracks in the soft earth, made the previous morning, were the only human footprints found. There was no sign that a vehicle had turned back at the heliport; instead, two sets of tire tracks led directly on into the sanctuary.

Recalling that a condor was said to have been photographed at close range while perched in a tree, I asked the two officials to view the surrounding chaparral for trees that stood above the brush. We agreed that within a distance of about half a mile there was no growth that stood over twelve feet.

Continuing on and reaching a point in good view of the nesting territory, we sighted two adult condors perched on the crest of a high rimrock above the nesting cliff. Stopping to study them, I explained to the officials that in the usual fieldwork of the condor study we avoided being seen by nesting condors at distances nearer than a mile, but the need to complete this investigation seemed crucial enough to warrant closer approach.

Reaching the end of the old roadway where the truck had been parked, we took the dim, abandoned trail that led toward the nest. Here I called upon the two rangers to inspect the human footprints that in places were well imprinted in the moist earth. The tracks led on about a quarter of a mile, ending at a point directly under the nesting cliff. I took a picture of the historic area, and as the two condors now circled overhead, we turned back and were out of the critical territory as quickly as possible.

I appreciated having these officials of the Forest Service accompany me in this review. But I was disappointed in their obvious indifference toward the details of the evidence involved. Their attitude reminded me of an old cow dog I once owned who grew lazy in his later years. He knew well the work of rounding up cattle and what was meant when he was called upon to bring a far-ranging animal back to the herd. At times, however, as he grew older, when ordered to fetch a cow that was off some distance, he would make a great show of eagerness and willingness while looking in every direction except that of the far cow. Soon learning the basis of this apparent blindness I would call him in during one of these demonstrations, give one of his ears a few sharp twists, and again firmly repeat the order. Immediately, without another glance one way or the other, the chastised shepherd would line out and bring in the cow. Observing the two rangers as they seemed to be scrutinizing everything in sight but the obvious facts I wanted them to witness, I could readily have twisted their ears.

A few months later, in June of 1964, when it was evident that the old nest had been abandoned, my brother and I examined the historic cave. We found bones, feathers, and excrement that seemed to indicate a nesting within at least the previous five years. However, there were also fragments of eggshell on the floor of the cave. This seemed to indicate that a nesting failure had occurred, probably during the previous few months.

This historic nesting territory was notorious for its invasions and failures. Our interpretation of Koford's report suggests that the work of a trail crew near the cave in 1940 caused an egg to be punctured. In 1939 a young bird, last seen as it left this nest, was presumed to have died shortly afterward. In 1960, long after the area was made a sanctuary, various other irregularities caused disturbance in the territory. These included the hauling of deer to the nearby *potrero* as bait for the condors, together with the activities of another photographer. The bulldozed firebreak, opening a route for invading humans, brought ruin to this high nesting retreat of the condors, even though it was within a specially protected part of the Sespe Refuge.

A few days after the Bucksnort episode I submitted a written report on the subject to the Forest Supervisor. About three weeks later the Supervisor responded with a report that upheld the claim of the condor warden and minimized the significance of the photographic operations. It claimed that although the sanctuary had been illegally entered, the trespass went only as far as the heliport. It explained the trip to the high peak as a search for trespassers by the warden, all in spite of the conclusive evidence to the contrary I had carefully pointed out to the inspecting rangers.

The photographer's illustrated story of his trip to the condor sanctuary was later published in his company's magazine, which the Forest Service characterized as a "conservation publication" with a circulation of a million readers. I found the article of particular interest. I had looked forward to seeing how it might confirm my version of what had been necessary to get the pictures. But the published pictures showed only flying condors against an open sky and two mounted specimens in a museum display. A photograph of the high peak above the condor nests showed no foreground that might disclose the point from which the picture was taken. Neither was there any picture of a condor in a tree or of the cattle on the high *potrero* where I had found the truck. But spread across the first pages of the article was a big, indistinct picture of a flying condor against the sky. Obviously it was taken at close range and in poor light. It made me think of the flashbulb I had picked up under the roosting tree near the old nest.

This magazine's account of the expedition stated with pointed emphasis that particular care had been taken to avoid trespassing in the sanctuary. In noting this, I recalled that the Forest Service had at least admitted that trespass had been committed. Thus did I learn about men while studying condors!

Chapter XIII

SHOWDOWN
in the SESPE

EARLY IN THIS STORY, I TOLD OF MY TRIP TO
the high peak in the condor refuge on the day that I picked up the
discarded carton of a flashbulb. At that time a project was under
consideration that was to become a foremost threat to condor
preservation. This was the project to dam the Sespe Canyon at a
point just before it entered the condor sanctuary.

From my high observation point that day, the lower and wilder
reaches of Sespe Canyon were close below and to the west. This last
stretch of the canyon, about eight miles across from ridge to ridge,
makes up the greater portion of the condor refuge. Except for a
public trail that allows fishing and hiking along the length of the
stream, the canyon is mostly inaccessible wilderness. It is in striking
contrast to the urban area into which it opens on the south.

I don't know of any other stream in southern California the size of Sespe Creek that remains undammed. Nor do I know of any other water course anywhere that compares with this wild, twisted, rock-walled canyon. Located, almost in surrealistical fashion, near the northern edge of one of the world's most bizarre metropolitan developments, the crooked Sespe is fantastic beyond anything man has yet constructed. Even if it were not a main haunt of the California condor, the area would be worthy of care and preservation as an incomparable piece of wild country.

At various points of its development, urban growth in the Los Angeles area had been limited by the supply of water. This limiting factor had steadily been overcome by bringing additional supplies from other areas, some from regions hundreds of miles distant. But as more water became available, new growth progressively outstripped the new supply and occasioned new demands.

In May of 1964, as I looked toward the south from the high peak in the condor refuge, the proliferating urban encroachment from that direction forced itself on the eye. Early in the day, before the smog had thickened in the Santa Clara Valley, I could see strange white fields in the brush-covered hills toward the southeast. Through the telescope it could be seen that the brown chaparral on these rough areas had recently been replaced by a dense cover of light-colored houses.

On a recent visit to a big feed lot near Castaic Junction, toward the east end of the Santa Clara Valley, I learned that a housing tract was soon to replace that extensive livestock development, which had included a big feed mill and several acres of pens where 17,000 steers could be fattened at one time.

At the west end of the valley, along points of the highway near the town of Ventura, the mountains of the condor country can be seen toward the east, rising in bold relief above an incongruous sea of new rooftops. Each time I passed along this route during my study of the condor, the rows of new dwellings seemed to have spread over more rich bottom land. Artificially established to house those working in industries mainly supported by federal appropriations, this type of population development and growth has become central to business promotion throughout the urban portions of California.

In its northward spread from the Los Angeles area, this urban population was reaching the territory just south of the condor refuge. It was purportedly running short of water, and as a solution was demanding a dam in Sespe Canyon. However, the proposed dam, involving appropriations of almost $100,000,000 in public funds, appeared to be an end in itself, seeming almost as much the objective of the promotion as was the additional water. The commercial and urban growth that would result from the funds made available for the work of the project were main points in the arguments supporting the enterprise.

The plan for water development was evidently projected right up to the point of final approval, on the assumption that various basic concepts and regulations of the Sespe Condor Sanctuary could be readily circumvented or annulled. A public road from Fillmore to the proposed dam would provide access through the center of the condor refuge for mass recreation. Such an influx to the dam, which would lie close to the north boundary of the refuge and across a main condor flight lane, would violate the sanctuary, frustrate its purpose, and destroy its function. From what we already knew about condor ecology, such a project, if allowed, could well bring doom to the already highly endangered species.

Various questions passed through my mind as I compared the wilderness of Sespe Canyon to the situation off toward the south. How long could the water of the creek—not a great amount—satisfy the accelerating demands of the advancing megalopolis? In a little over a hundred years, what had been a remote Mexican outpost, inhabited by a few whites and a sparse scattering of native Indians, had grown as no other human establishment had ever been known to grow. If its uncontrolled proliferation now required the damming of the last wild canyon in its surrounding region, how long would such a resource keep it growing? And what would be the means of further proliferation? In consideration of real human welfare, was it not time to think of regulation and control rather than of more growth and development? And as a last means of such control, what could be more practicable and effective than to leave undisturbed and undeveloped this last wild local canyon and its natural flow of water?

Ultimately the Sespe Sanctuary, if it remains an inviolate area set aside for the condors, will serve equally as a most practicable measure of restraint and control, protecting man's habitat from ecological bankruptcy. Ultimately, condor preservation helps to assure human survival.

By the time our survey was completed, the need and effectiveness of the Sespe Refuge as a home for the condor had been repeatedly confirmed. A comparatively tiny area in the species' occupied range, this territory functioned as a main focal point of all condor activity. At times it appeared that the only known nesting territories in which breeding condors and their young would be safe from being shot were located within this inviolate area. Reminders of what the birds owed to this project were the museum specimens of six condors—two family groups—that were shot there by hired collectors in the years from 1917 to 1920. These birds were all killed in lower Sespe Canyon in a nesting territory that is now a part of the condor sanctuary. Nonbreeding birds also returned in fall and winter to this favorite retreat. Obviously the area offered peculiar advantages to all the condors at one time or another throughout each year.

Incompetence in the management of the Sespe Sanctuary could well have given rise to cynicism and despair. But it was inspiring to find condors, as we found them, still represented by a viable breeding stock that was reproducing at a normal rate, and in all ways demonstrating an almost miraculous capacity for survival. The problem of saving the condor was, then, mainly giving it the protection it was supposed to be receiving.

Despite the discrepancies in its management, the Sespe Sanctuary had not been ineffective. From my observations I would say that at the time of our survey every living condor owed its survival in one way or another to the workings of this remarkable conservation project. Probably not all the birds had been hatched and reared in the refuge, and some may not have used it extensively as winter quarters; but without this main center for the social activity in which pairs could form and nonbreeding groups could become organized, I do not believe the species could have held out.

After pointing out the deplorable weaknesses of the condor-preservation effort, it may seem inconsistent to be calling attention to its strength. But it is the achievement represented in the condor program that makes its failings so conspicuous and so in need of critical analysis and review. This legacy of conservation achievement and success, which is confirmed in and symbolized by every living condor, must be continually renewed and safeguarded. It was at stake in the proposal to build a dam in Sespe Canyon and construct a public highway through the heart of the condor sanctuary.

At the completion of our fieldwork in the fall of 1964, Alden Miller presented a summary of the main findings before a convention of the National Audubon Society in Tucson, Arizona. Present at this gathering was an official delegation from the Sespe area who had come to hear Dr. Miller's views on their dam project. Dr. Miller's statement included the following paragraphs:

"The Sespe refuge has been and is crucial to the condor's survival, but as a refuge it has been barely enough. We need to hold rigorously what is now set out as protected land and we need to augment it by properly set up, permanent buffer areas and wilderness areas. The access corridors of the refuge were to have limited use; these limitations should be rigorously reaffirmed. To yield and open these corridors to water developments and to through traffic and construction would destroy the efficacy of the refuge.

"The buffer and primitive areas should be permanently closed to hunting. Group camps, concessions, and mass recreational facilities in the corridors and in the Agua Blanca and Sweetwater drainages at the northern border of the Sespe refuge should be ruled out; there must be no yielding to development of a dam and a lake in that area."

I could appreciate the surprise of the dam promoters at this confrontation in Tucson. Suddenly it seemed that the myth of condor preservation had vanished, and in its place was the real thing. This was demonstrated by the strong response of the assembled conservationists to Alden Miller's candid recommendations.

Following this confrontation, the proponents of the dam immediately launched a publicity campaign intended to discredit the condor program. The economic welfare of an exploding human population was of more importance, it was proclaimed, than a few ugly vultures and the interests of a few bird watchers. But this disparagement of the condor failed, and the attackers then turned to berating the conservationists for allowing the rare species to have declined by a third in two decades. Suddenly the developers presented themselves in the role of condor protectors, far more competent, they claimed, than the conservation forces who were opposing the dam.

A motley assortment of interests were recruited and organized to work with the proponents of the dam toward breaking down the defense of those in favor of the condor refuge. The recreation industry, the construction trade and real-estate dealers were prominent in this coalition. Among the forces arrayed against the condor there was also, paradoxically, a quite influential faction from the realm of ornithology.

In the broad field of bird study there is a vocal and politically active element that confines its understanding of ecology and conservation to what is known of caged birds. The principles of condor preservation, as this faction would practice them, would operate mainly in zoos or similar man-made facilities. The would-be condor keepers are influential and well financed, as they demonstrated in the project to trap a pair of condors back in 1953. They have remained a formidable threat to the idea of preserving the condor as a wild, free-living species—a symbol of wilderness and of real survival. When this faction combines, as it did, with the powerful, economic forces promoting a dam in Sespe Canyon, the danger to the condor program is greatly augmented.

With the advice and cooperation of the condor cagers, the developers embroidered their proposal of becoming fairy godfathers to the condors. The starvation fallacy was again brought up to support an argument for a program of artificial feeding, which would be carried out in conjunction with the development and operation of the water project. A plan was offered for breeding the birds in captivity.

Fortunately, we were able to meet these arguments and notions with the up-to-date facts that we had gathered in our fieldwork. Using this material, together with the previous findings of Koford's research, we showed that the condors had ample food in their range and that their survival needs would not be met by raising them like chickens.

One of the main effects of our arguments was a surprising increase in popular ecological understanding. As had been dramatically demonstrated in the response to Alden Miller's recommendations at the Audubon Convention in Tucson, an unforeseen swell of public opinion appeared in support of our position on how and why the condor should be protected. The conservation philosophy out of

21. *(Above)* On the trail to the condor nest in the Sespe Sanctuary, two officials of Los Padres National Forest following the tracks made by two human invaders, one a photographer, within the protected area.
22. *(Below)* Sunning, a morning exercise of condors.

23. *(Above)* Peering at the photographer, this nesting condor shows the swelling of the jaws which develops in parent condors that are feeding young. 24. *(Below)* The inability of condors to grasp with the feet can be noted in this adult as it takes off from the entrance of a nest cave.

25. *(Above)* Nesting sites are usually situated where the big birds can make a downward, open takeoff. 26. *(Below)* Condors usually alight on a convenient perch prior to entering the nesting cave.

27. *(Above)* The California condor in captivity (a yearling bird captured in 1967 when still too young to fly well) 28. *(Below)* . . . and in the wild.

which the Sespe Sanctuary had materialized was spreading like a leaven through our society.

At the time of this writing, in the summer of 1967, the forces of condor preservation have successfully stood off the threat of the Sespe development project and associated dangers. The project required the passage of a local bond issue and the approval of different government authorities. In a vigorously contested election the bond issue was defeated by the people.

Chapter XIV

TEN THOUSAND YEARS
of SURVIVAL

AROUND 1907, WHEN JOSEPH GRINNELL WAS PRE-
paring to build the Museum of Vertebrate Zoology and when Kelly
Truesdale saw his first condor as it sailed across the Carrisa, there
was another epic beginning in another field of condor study. In that
year two other eager workers in the field of natural history took a
historic streetcar ride to the outskirts of Los Angeles. One of the
pair was John C. Merriam, who was establishing a department of
paleontology at the University of California. The other, a younger
man, was Loye Miller, a teacher of biology at the Los Angeles
Normal School, and the father of an infant son named Alden.

The two young naturalists stepped off the streetcar and walked
through an open grain field to a little, tumbledown ranch house.
Near this building was a small pit where some old bones had been
dug out. The two men examined the pit, picking up and scrutiniz-

ing some of the excavated material. The location was a place called Rancho La Brea, and the two naturalists had come to investigate the deposit of fossil bones.

During the three years following this first investigation, Loye Miller devoted all the time he could spare from his teaching duties to digging and collecting at the La Brea deposits. Several thousand years before his time, during the geologic epoch known as the Pleistocene, a seepage of heavy oil had welled up through cracks in the surface strata and settled in natural depressions, forming many pools of various shapes and depths. As it dried in the sun and weather, the heavy oil became steadily more thick and tarlike. In some cases these pools were hidden, perhaps by a coating of dust or leaves, or covered by water that might be drinkable. Some probably had marshlike vegetation around the edges. These hidden or disguised pools had apparently worked as natural traps to catch and entomb the birds and mammals that became mired in the sticky ooze. From the bones of the entombed creatures, preserved virtually unchanged, the modern paleontologist has been able to interpret the meaning of the Rancho La Brea fossil beds almost as clearly as if he had been an eyewitness to the age-long drama of which they are a record.

Loye Miller has explained how the slowly sinking carcasses of unsuspecting beasts caught in the "villainously sticky" asphalt attracted carnivores, large and small. Flesh-eating birds, especially the carrion feeders, were also attracted and trapped. All became part of the natural collection. Predominant among the entombed birds were the golden eagle and the ancestral condor, *Gymnogyps amplus*. This extinct relative of the present-day condor flourished during a period near the end of the Pleistocene Epoch over 10,000 years ago, and there is some evidence that it ranged eastward across what is now the southern United States as far as Florida.

But the records of these prehistoric condors have a more important meaning than what they reveal of distribution. Through the new process of carbon-14 dating, the condor bones of the La Brea tar pits have been found to be much younger than was previously assumed. The wood of a small tree that was growing in one of the pits when it first became a pool of liquid tar was found to be approximately 14,500 years old. Fossil bones packed solidly around the trunk and above the roots of this tree were of the typical Rancho

La Brea fauna of which the ancestral condor is a characteristic species. This new information was published in 1960 in a scientific paper by Dr. Hildegarde Howard, a colleague of Loye Miller and also a foremost authority on the La Brea collections.

Previous to the carbon-14 dating, the famous fossil beds had been scientifically considered to be "approximately 50,000 years old" and the same age was quite logically assumed for the associated condor bones. On this scientific assumption the California condor has been generally characterized as a decrepit, fading relic of a remote, geologic past.

A profoundly different concept of condor evolution now seems in order as a result of the new dating. Even before the new age determination there was research which called for a new outlook on condor survival. In a study made in the 1940's it was demonstrated that the condors now living belong to a new species, different and probably younger than the condor which left its bones in the La Brea tar pits. The bones of the La Brea collections show a species larger and specifically different in the structure of its skull than the present condor. On the basis of this last fundamental difference the extinct condor of Pleistocene time is scientifically listed under the name *Gymnogyps amplus*. Its close relative and probable descendant, the present living condor, has the name *Gymnogyps californianus*. Instead of "a dying relict of the Pleistocene" the California condor now appears to be more a creature of the present and hopefully the future.

Among some of the best authorities on the subject there is a question whether the difference between *Gymnogyps amplus* and *Gymnogyps californianus* is sufficient to qualify the two as separate species. This question could, with equal reason, be applied to many other closely related species and indeed to some species which are scientifically classified as belonging to different genera. I have in mind, for instance, a fertile female cross between an American bison of the genus *Bison,* and a Hereford cow of the genus *Bos.* This female cattalo which was reared on a ranch in my own neighborhood has produced two calves from Hereford sires.

The research on which the condors of the Pleistocene and those of Recent times have been scientifically classified as separate species seems to be exceptionally thorough. It was carried out by Harvey I. Fisher, an eminent zoologist who studied at the Museum of

Vertebrate Zoology. In a paper published in 1944 in *The Condor,* Fisher demonstrated in detail the differences in bone structure, both quantitative and qualitative, between the two forms. In determining whether these forms characterized two different species, Fisher wrote: "That *Gymnogyps amplus* is not a subspecies of *G. californianus* is indicated by the absence of overlap in the ranges and ratios of certain characters in the relatively stable basitemporal region of the skull and by the major qualitative differences already discussed." This scientific classification has stood without change for well over twenty years, and seems now to be fairly widely accepted.

There seems to be no concrete evidence that the California condor existed in its present form prior to the Recent geologic epoch, or roughly the last ten thousand years. Carl Koford, in listing the prehistoric records of the condor, gave places in Texas, New Mexico, Nevada, Oregon, and California where subfossil remains of the present species have been found. Significantly, he noted that the age of the bones found at the different localities was variously estimated at from 500 to 3,000 years. Man had been in these areas much longer, and Koford noted that at some localities the condor bones were found associated with human cultural materials and with the bones of now extinct mammals.

Since all the condor remains found in the Rancho La Brea collections are classified as belonging to the earlier, Pleistocene form, it seems evident that the present-day species was not in that area until after the tar pits ceased to trap and entomb condors. This raises some pertinent questions. When, where, and how did the condor of today come into existence? What is its relationship to the slightly different and probably older Rancho La Brea bird? Is it a direct descendant or not?

Harvey Fisher wrote: "One must either assume that *Gymnogyps californianus* has evolved as a species since the Pleistocene or that it has moved into the area since the Pleistocene." He added: "*Gymnogyps amplus* might well be considered the progenitor of *Gymnogyps californianus*."

Through the new means of dating prehistoric material, a conspicuous correlation has appeared between two epic events in condor survival. With the advent of man as an associate of the condor, which evidently occurred around the close of the Pleistocene epoch, *Gymnogyps amplus,* the condor of the Rancho La Brea tar pits, vanished into extinction along with a host of its contemporaries. Another member of this fantastic prehistoric cavalcade was the great vulture *Teraternis,* which was larger than the condor and may have been the largest bird that has ever flown. The coming of man to the area also coincided with the disappearance of such large herbivores as the bison, the horse, the camel, the mammoth and the giant ground sloth. Among the predators that passed into extinction along with these food species were the wolf, the lion, and the big sabertooth cat.

Although this was long before man had the gun, this new and most effective predator had other weapons. Also, he had the torch with which to fire the primeval grasslands and forests. In a natural realm that had evolved without adaptation to the human, the impact of this new agent of ecologic revolution must have been profound. There may be an analogy between the extinction of various prehistoric species in the Los Angeles region some ten thousand years ago and the recent wiping out by human beings with guns of the American bison, the passenger pigeon, and the California grizzly. Perhaps the first human invaders to reach the condor country found the bigger condor of the Pleistocene time vulnerable and easy to exterminate. Perhaps it is adaptation to human predation that has produced the condor of today.

The first written record of the California condor appears in the diary of a Spanish friar who was a member of the Sebastián Vizcaíno expedition exploring the coast of California in 1602. The friar saw and described what was evidently a group of condors feeding on the carcass of a whale on the beach at Monterey Bay. For 167 years following this first account, nothing further about condors appears in the record until the historic Gaspar de Portolá expedition of 1769. This Spanish land force, traveling north from San Diego, had camped a few miles east of Monterey Bay. They found there an encampment of native Indians who, according to the diary of one of the Spaniards, had recently captured a condor as part of a tribal ritual. Judging by the description, the bird was evidently an immature not yet full grown. It was finally killed in the course of the ritual, and the skin was then stuffed with straw to be kept in that state for some time. The Spaniards, impressed by the large size of this stuffed bird and by the ritual, named the small stream that passed nearby, Río del Pájaro (river of the bird). The stream and the valley through which it flows still retain that early name.

The details of another ceremony are described in an article on the customs and traditions of the native Indians living around Mission San Juan Capistrano, between Los Angeles and San Diego. This document confirms a practice that was common among the Indians. Evidently the ritual use of condors depleted their numbers for thousands of years before the white man with his gun first entered the condor range.

In the Indian ceremony a large bird, usually a condor, was first brought forth and placed on a structure serving as an altar. The live bird was then made the object of adoration expressed by the younger, unmarried females of the gathering. Then, with all the tribe joining in a dancing, singing procession, the condor was carried on its altar to another place of assemblage, a sort of temple. Here, as a climax of the rite, it was killed in some way without loss of blood or feathers. The skin was then removed to become a relic or ceremonial garment, and the carcass was buried at a spot within the place of worship. The burial was accompanied by a special ceremony in which the older women, gathering together in a group, moaned and wailed in sorrow and anguish.

It appears that the condor was a first choice of the Indians as the bird to be used in their rituals. Loye Miller found a surprising proportion of condor bones among bird remains collected from a prehistoric Indian midden near The Dalles in north-central Oregon, on the Columbia River. Among the raptorial birds represented, only the bald eagle outnumbered the condor. Both eagles and condors probably found this a favorite foraging range during the season when salmon were spawning and dying along the banks of the great river. The remains at The Dalles, discovered after the time of Koford's study were not reported on by Loye Miller until 1957. Carbon-14 tests set the age of these condor bones at slightly less than 8,000 years and make them the oldest known record of *Gymnogyps californianus*.

Previously, subfossil remains of *Gymnogyps californianus* had been variously estimated at from 500 to 3,000 years. Possibly carbon-14 tests of these specimens would show them to be older. Also, the midden at The Dalles was located on the western border of an extensive region where condors, although absent in historic times, might have previously occurred. Remarking on these bones found at The Dalles, Miller pointed out that the same species of condor may have inhabited the region immediately to the east in late Pleistocene or early Recent time. This is an important point in considering whether or not the present condor evolved since the Pleistocene age or moved into its present range from some outside territory some time in the last 10,000 years. At any rate, Loye Miller's paper on the Oregon Indian midden, published in 1957, indicates most clearly that man has been a predator of *Gymnogyps californianus* for much longer than was previously supposed. Possibly men were killing condors throughout the time that the present-day bird evolved.

Extensive studies of bird remains in various Indian middens in western America allowed Loye Miller to give a comprehensive account of different uses made of birds by primitive man beginning ten to twelve thousand years ago: "His aesthetics, religion, ceremonials, his social organizations, interests in pets or games, craftsmanship in clothing, housing, weapon-making and I know not what else, all had an influence upon the accumulation of bird bones aside from his mere desire for food, though the latter may have loomed large."

This long association in which condors, wherever found, were human association and influence seem to represent a prime factor influencing numbers, distribution, behavior, and ultimately the species' survival. One authority on the subject commented that the demand for nestling condors was such that a nest was considered the inviolate property of the Indian who found it and became a personal possession of the greatest value, to be handed down from father to son. Condor feathers for use in dress and costume were in extensive demand as well as the birds themselves. Altogether the human association and influence seem to represent a prime factor of condor evolution. Down through the thousands of years this steady attrition could have worked as a selective force in which the ability to avoid man would become a main factor of survival and a strong characteristic among the surviving condors.

In this selective process, birds choosing the most hidden and inaccessible nesting places would rear the most young. Where this choice represented inherent behavior, the trait would be passed on to succeeding generations. Steadily the predilection to nest beyond the reach of humans would become characteristic. Through this process of adaptation the range of the condor would become restricted to places offering nesting and roosting refuge beyond the reach of human beings, but within year-round cruising range of an adequate supply of available food.

This speculation brings to mind the thoughts of Kelly Truesdale and William Leon Dawson, the two pioneer egg collectors, as they crouched at the entrance of the cave nest, back in 1911, and pondered why a small nestling condor would be so alarmed at their presence and have such a frightening voice.

The early Spanish explorers and colonists of California were evidently not so much interested in hunting or natural history as the American frontiersmen who came west across the mountains. The early British, however, collected extensively to record and appraise the biological resources of the new Pacific region. In 1792, the British ship *Discovery,* under Captain George Vancouver, remained anchored for over a month at Monterey. The official surgeon on board this vessel, a Scot by the name of Archibald Menzies, was also a qualified naturalist and scientific collector. And so he was assigned the task of chronicling the natural resources found in the course of the voyage.

While hunting game with Spanish officials from the Presidio at Monterey, Menzies collected the California condor and the California quail. Skins of these, which went to a British museum, were the first specimens of either species to be placed in a scientific collection, and both birds received their scientific names from these historic specimens. But aside from the zoological aspects of this first condor skin, there is another, of even deeper significance. Taken in excursions that combined both hunting and collecting, it represents the earliest scientific proof of the gun as a new factor in condor mortality and of condor evolution.

Only a little more than a decade after Menzies collected and prepared the first scientific specimen of a condor, another important condor discovery was made by an even more historic exploration. In the fall of 1805, as the members of the Lewis and Clark Expedition, moving down the Columbia River, were about to become the first white Americans to reach the Pacific Ocean from the east across the mountains, they became the first Americans to record the sighting of a California condor.

Several of the great birds appeared as the explorers reached a point just above the cascades of the Columbia some thirty miles west of The Dalles. Recording the new bird in his journal, William Clark, co-leader of the expedition, noted the unmistakable size of the great vultures and the characteristic patches of white under the wings.

Clark mentioned that Captain Lewis attempted to shoot one of the condors. Thus, in this second historic discovery of the condor by men with guns, the first act was to put the new implement of condor adversity into immediate action. This would remain a popular and almost spontaneous procedure for at least the next hundred years; with no effective counter move until 1908, when an aroused group of egg collectors, of which Joseph Grinnell was a leader, brought a surprised condor shooter into a Los Angeles court.

After this first sighting, condors were noted at various times throughout the winter and early spring of 1805–1806, which the party of Lewis and Clark spent near the mouth of the Columbia. On at least three occasions condors were shot and brought to camp by members of the expedition who were hunting game. One of these was a wounded bird which was described in detail in the journal of Captain Lewis. The measured wingspread of this live bird was recorded as being nine feet two inches. Its length from tip of beak to end of toe was reported three feet nine and a half inches. The bird's weight was given as twenty-five pounds. Except for the unusually heavy weight, the size given for this specimen is about the average of condors measured since that time.

Captain Meriwether Lewis, the commanding officer of the expedition, was a talented amateur naturalist. His detailed description of the wounded condor, which included a sketch of the bird's head and upper neck, still seems remarkably accurate today. This is all the more unusual in that it is the first on record to give written details of the characteristic features of a live condor.

Returning up the Columbia on their homeward journey overland to St. Louis, the Lewis and Clark party noted their last condor on April 6, 1806, at a point not far from where they had first seen the species the previous fall. This last bird was also shot by one of the explorers while hunting.

Two decades after the Lewis and Clark Expedition, condors were noted and collected along the lower Columbia by other explorers.

Two Scotch naturalists, Davis Douglas and John Scouler, who visited the area about 1826, sent condor skins back to England as further scientific evidence of the new species. With the skin that had been collected at Monterey by Menzies over thirty years before, these specimens from the Columbia were the only evidence of the condor yet known to science. Lewis and Clark had been able to bring back only a skull and a primary wing feather. These were placed in an American museum as evidence of the great new bird they had discovered in the Far West.

In his diary, Douglas wrote about collecting the condors by shooting them with buckshot. The head of one bird was so damaged by a charge of the big shot that it was not preserved as a specimen. Trying to avoid such damage, he later "fired at many of them with every kind of smaller shot, but without effect." He also observed that the condors could be taken in steel traps. John Scouler told in his journal of obtaining condors from the local Indians in return for tobacco.

The records of Douglas and Scouler are important, as they confirm the continued occurrence of condors during the early 1800's as far north along the Pacific Coast as the lower Columbia River. But they also confirm the growing impact of the gun as a new factor affecting the numbers, distribution, and behavior of a bird that was evidently rare even at that time. It should not be overlooked, however, that most of this early collecting was done to establish scientific knowledge about a little-known species. The program of condor preservation that would later develop as the final hope of condor survival would be based on the factual information being gathered through such collecting.

Condors became rare, and evidently disappeared from the Columbia River shortly after the visit of Douglas and Scouler. In 1934 two American naturalists, Dr. John Kirk Townsend and Thomas Nuttall, came down the great river with the Nathaniel Wyeth Oregon Expedition. This party of Americans was one of the first to make the trip overland to the Pacific after the trail-blazing explorations of Lewis and Clark. Townsend, a professional ornithologist, was mainly interested in the birds of the new Oregon Country, ownership of which was still in dispute between England and the United States. While on the lower Columbia he prepared the first skin of a condor to reach an American museum.

But though Townsend collected quite extensively in the area, he rarely saw more than "two or three" condors at a time. Apparently the only condor he was able to shoot was a single immature bird. While a few unsubstantiated observations have been reported since, this seems to be the last positive record of the species in Oregon. Within three decades after their first discovery by the white man, the condors of the Columbia River were gone.

The history of condors in the region of northwestern Oregon, while showing the northern limits of the bird's historic range, also raises some interesting questions bearing on condor survival. Were the condors of the Columbia in 1805 a migrant number foraging north along the coast from a main center of distribution in California? If so, what caused these birds to discontinue their extensive northward movements? Or were the birds found by Lewis and Clark members of a resident, isolated population, breeding and remaining permanently in the region? If so, again what caused their quick disappearance?

Carl Koford, recognizing the importance of the Columbia River records, noted that foraging condors tend to search over the same area for many days in succession. He remarked that "the presence of two or three dozen condors in northwestern Oregon would be sufficient to account for all the records for that area." He further pointed out that there was no evidence of the breeding of condors north of San Francisco.

It seemed probable to Koford that the birds along the Columbia were drifters from the breeding range in California. In the early nineteenth century condors were known to feed on dead marine life along the coast at Monterey. Nonbreeding birds following this coastal food supply northward could easily have reached the Columbia. The big scavengers were also known to range the Sacramento Valley until the 1860's. From there they might cross into central Oregon and soar down the Willamette Valley to the Columbia.

Food conditions in California may have caused the condors to move northward in their foraging. Finding an abundant supply along the Columbia, they would tend to stay or return in subsequent years. With livestock increasing in California during the Mission Era, however, a new and abundant food supply developed in the south. The condors of the Columbia might then have moved back toward the center of their breeding range and discontinued their extensive northern movements.

But none of the records of condors on the Columbia were for the summer season. This was odd for the run of salmon occurred there during early summer. It would seem that condors moving north from California would do so in summer and not in winter. However, with dead salmon along the great river for a hundred miles, the big vultures could have been scattered during this time of food abundance so as not to be noticed by the early explorers.

In his 1953 report, Koford mentioned the possibility that the condors of northwestern Oregon were the remnant of a formerly widespread population in that region. But at that time no fossil or subfossil specimens were in evidence to support the idea. However, when Loye Miller reported his identification of the prehistoric condor bones from the Indian midden at The Dalles in 1957 it strengthened the possibility that the condors along the Columbia were remnants of a resident northern population which may have been the ancestral stock of *G. californianus*. The Recent, or present-day, California condor could thus have come originally from this region of the Pacific Northwest to take over the condor range of California, left vacant by the passing of *G. amplus*.

The gun may well outweigh all other factors as the cause of the condor's disappearance from the Columbia. Clearly the species was shot at every opportunity. This would have drastic effects on a local population, either migrant or resident, that might well have numbered no more than "two or three dozen birds." The city of Astoria, at the mouth of the Columbia, was founded in 1811 by John Jacob Astor, a New York fur merchant. The fur brigades were then wiping the beaver from the streams of the West. The new trading outpost on the Columbia must have been a center of trapping and hunting activity. Douglas, in his journal, mentioned that the wing feathers of condors were "highly prized by the Canadian voyageurs for making the stems of their tobacco pipes." In my view, then, what mainly caused the disappearance of condors on the Columbia was the introduction of that new implement of condor mortality—the gun.

The wave of empire that swept westward following the Lewis and Clark Expedition brought an increasing number of scientific collectors into the Pacific region. Most of these were attached to official or military explorations, and nearly all were in search of specimens. The Califorma condor was one of the main objectives in some of these collecting expeditions. Also, after the first period of settlement, local interests, both public and private, became active in the search for the skins and eggs of the condor. This popular interest in matters of natural history produced the egg-collecting fraternity to which Kelly Truesdale later belonged.

With this early wave of exploration and settlement, the range of the condor steadily drew in toward its prehistoric center in the region of southern coastal California. We have noted that Koford determined that the condors were gone from the Columbia by 1840. By the 1860's the birds were extinct or very rare in the Sacramento Valley, and by 1890 they had practically disappeared from all their former range north of San Francisco.

In the south only a few unsubstantiated reports of condors were made in San Diego County after 1910. The species had nested in that county as late as 1900, and at least eighteen specimens were taken there between 1875 and 1900. Farther south, across the Mexican border in Baja California, a few sightings of condors were reported as late as 1932. But in Koford's fieldwork of the 1940's he found no evidence that the species had been in that southern region in recent years. The birds had once ranged as far south as two hundred miles below the Mexican border.

There is no evidence that the condor has been abundant at any time since the coming of the white man. During the 1800's, various naturalists making expeditions from Europe and the eastern United States with a main purpose of obtaining specimens of the new and distinctive species failed. One of them was János Xántus, the Hungarian naturalist, who collected nine grizzly bears while exploring the condor range of central California in 1857. More than a dozen collectors who were active in California before 1860 never got a specimen of a condor. While some written records described condors as being abundant, it seems important to mention again that a small number of the great birds foraging and feeding conspicuously in a particular area can give the appearance of a greater number.

It was not until 1859, sixty-seven years after Archibald Menzies collected the first scientific specimen of a condor at Monterey, that the first occupied condor nest known to science was found in the same region. Prior to this discovery, various fanciful descriptions of condor nests and eggs had been offered by otherwise eminent authorities. One highly regarded account had the birds laying a jet-black egg. The urge to be the first to discover a nest and egg of the new species was undoubtedly strong among the early naturalists and hunters. The fact that this discovery was not made until a decade after the beginning of the California Gold Rush is further evidence that the condor was already rare when the white man arrived.

The status of the condor population during historic time is thus best indicated by the demand and search for specimens that continued up to about 1920. About then, either from legal restrictions or scarcity of the birds, or both, the collecting of condors and their eggs finally came to an end. With nearly all specimens of the species or their eggs now on record in various collections, Carl Koford found evidence of no more than sixty eggs and about 130 skins or mounted specimens in all. In view of the extensive searching for condor skins and eggs from the time that the first specimen was collected in 1792 until the last skins and eggs were permitted to be taken around 1920, the amount collected does not seem to indicate that the species was abundant at any time.

In the late 1800's the main center and common breeding territory for condors appears to have been the coastal region of southern Monterey County, approximately in the middle of the California coast. The early records indicate that this area had been a preferred territory for a long time. The San Antonio Mission and the big Spanish ranchos in the Salinas Valley grazed great numbers of livestock. Adjacent to these grazing lands were the rugged chaparral-covered Santa Lucia Mountains. The first condor nest to be found by a white man was located in these coastal mountains of Monterey County. At least eight condor eggs and three young birds were collected in this territory between 1895 and 1902, mainly by local professional hunters and collectors. The last specimen from the area was taken in 1917. After about 1920, only a few sightings of condors have been reported from this area.

The history of the birds in western Monterey County is analogous to the disappearance of condors on the Columbia River. Questioned by Carl Koford in 1940, various older residents of the region expressed the belief that instead of being killed off the condors had moved to other areas. The time of greatest decrease was variously placed from 1890 to 1910. However, it was during this period that three young birds and eight eggs were known to have been taken in the area. There is no way of knowing how many condors were shot for one reason or another during the same time.

There seems to be no evidence that food shortage was a factor in the disappearance of condors from this northern section of their traditional breeding range. Sufficient cause can be found in the general movement of settlers into the area in the homesteading boom that began in the 1880's. Among these pioneers were professional hunters and collectors who made a business of selling condor eggs and skins. As with the condors of the Columbia River, it appears that human predation was the main cause of the disappearance of the condor from its ancestral range in western Monterey County.

In historic time condors have not been known to range inland from the coast more than about 150 miles. After the birds were gone from western Monterey County, for the next two decades the Sisquoc area, about 120 miles southward, was a favorite territory. The center has now moved toward the south, as Koford discovered when he found the focal point of all condor activity in the 1940's to be in southeastern Ventura County, where the Sespe Condor Sanctuary is now located.

About fifty miles farther south from the Sespe refuge are the historic tar pits of Rancho La Brea, where the Pleistocene relative of the California condor left dramatic evidence of its prehistoric existence. There may be ecological significance in the fact that the hard-pressed condors of today are finding their most secure retreat in the same general territory that was evidently a last center of abundance for their predecessors of around 10,000 years ago.

But there is another meaning in this odd situation where the condor now finds the last wherewithal for its survival. This ancestral home of the great bird lies in the same general area where condor preservation had its beginnings and has reached its greatest strength and development.

Chapter XV

A LAST LOOK AROUND

ONE VERY IMPORTANT THING CAN BE LEARNED
from the record of the past: If man chooses to do so, and with no
more than token sacrifice, he can live with the condor. Whether
modern man is capable of making this slight sacrifice may well
determine his own fitness for survival. The history of our thousands
of years with the condors was much in my mind on a recent trip I
took to Kelly Truesdale's old nesting site. I had two companions
with me on this pilgrimage, a leader of a local sportsmen's group
and a young college student. Although both were native residents of
the area and were sincere conservationists, neither had ever seen a
condor.

A road into Los Padres National Forest, built in the 1950's, now
reached to within about two miles of the old nest. Leaving our car
at the end of this road we took a steep trail to the top of a high ridge

that overlooked most of the surrounding region. Overgrown by chaparral, the only vehicles the trail would now accommodate were motorcycles. A short time previous to our visit it had been used in a cross-country motorcycle race. It was rutted and dusty from this heavy use.

I later questioned a local official of the Forest Service about this type of travel in this historic retreat of the condors. The answer was neither unexpected nor unusual. This was additional forest "use," I was told, and as such was approved and fostered by the forest authorities. Reaching a high point on the ridge, I left the beaten trail and led my companions a short distance through the chaparral to where a lone pine offered shade. It was June, and the morning sun was already warm. We would be watching from this high lookout for a few hours in the hope of seeing a condor.

But I had reasons other than comfort to leave the trail and watch from under the pine. Whether condors were in the area or not, I wanted my companions to see and feel for themselves why we should protect this historic condor retreat from further invasion and desecration. I wanted them to experience the feeling of wilderness. In remote places the whispering of even the lightest breeze in a pine stimulates this feeling.

Seeing no condors as the forenoon passed, we discussed the country around us. I pointed out Painted Rock, one of the historic landmarks on the Carrisa. This rock outcropping rises in the form of an amphitheater near the west side of the plains. A natural rock dwelling, it was evidently used for thousands of years as a favorite place of shelter and habitation by the California Indians, and its inner walls are decorated by the faded traces of ancient paintings. We speculated on the long period of some ten thousand years in which men and condors had lived together in this fabulous heartland of California.

Commenting on the human culture that left these symbols of its way of life, we shifted our attention to another local landmark and the symbols of our own culture. This recent development extended in a wide checkerboard of vacant streets and roadways from one side to the other of the ten-mile-wide Carrisa. It was one of the real-estate promotions that had in recent years become a salient feature of the California landscape.

In this particular development, one of the old cattle ranches on the

Carrisa had been bought and divided into plots of two and a half acres. Each plot was then sold as a "rancho" on the installment plan, at many times the previous purchase price. The main buyers of these homesites were people of low income living in congested areas who wanted to escape from the conditions of their own density. They were seeking the real freedom that is found only in uncrowded places.

Viewing this project from our high vantage point, we could see that only a very few of the little holdings had materialized into occupied homesites. Some that had were already abandoned. The Carrisa is not a place of moderate climate, and in this arid region water for domestic use is highly restricted. But the promotion had been efficient, and the little ranchos had sold readily. As measured in terms of modern economics, this enterprise probably represented the most successful business operation ever carried out on this superb stretch of open country.

This land deal and its obvious outcome offered a dramatic comparison to the idea and the fact of condor preservation. In my conversation with the young men, I compared the human attributes and achievements represented in the success of this real-estate enterprise with those represented in the prehistoric symbols on the walls of nearby Painted Rock. I further compared the human qualities and capabilities required in the success of the big land deal to those required for a land-use program in which the condor would remain a free-living associate of the human.

As we reviewed and discussed these graphic exhibits of different human endeavors and accomplishments, I could see that my companions were stirred. The college student was visibly eager: he saw the challenge in the scene before us. There were prospects of achievement far more exciting and rewarding than anything to be found in the money-grubbing activities that for over a hundred years had dominated land use in the condor country.

I was reminded of my own youthful excitement when I first came to the wild canyon with Kelly Truesdale back in 1921, and saw my first condor. I don't recall any other single experience that did more to impress me with the value of things other than money.

Noon was approaching, and no condors had appeared. We were ready to leave our observation point. As we rose to depart I mentioned how William Leon Dawson had looked out on this part of eastern San Luis Obispo County in 1911 and called it the heart of California. We agreed that after more than half a century, and in spite of the checkerboard of vacant streets that now stretched across the open Carrisa, Dawson's appraisal was still fitting. Explaining how condors ranged out from this ancestral stronghold, I pointed out Castle Mountain, forty miles away on the northern horizon. On the east from our high position we could see beyond the Temblor Range and across the San Joaquin to the snow-capped horizon of the Sierra Nevada. At the lower end of the Carrisa, where the Temblors fade into a range of low hills, smog was drifting westward from the San Joaquin Valley into a central part of the condor country.

An airplane was zooming back and forth somewhere in the hills along the west side of the Carrisa. It was evidently spraying the range with poison of some kind. Larkspur was blooming on the local ranges, and had been killing cattle. Perhaps the plane was spraying herbicide to control the poisonous plants. This would kill other range plants, including the native legumes on which the productivity of the land itself depended. The aircraft might have been spreading poisoned grain to kill ground squirrels—the latest technique to be introduced in the traditional squirrel-poisoning ritual was aerial application of the poisoned grain. Introduced as a measure of efficiency to replace manpower, the grain bait, treated with 1080 poison, was loaded into an airplane and scattered broadcast over the ranges.

In company with the agricultural official in charge, I had recently appraised one of the first operations of this new practice. The ecological impact on the general wildlife resource was appalling. But more appalling was the official ecological illiteracy that advocated and recommended this new practice.

I later wrote to the poison official, expressing my doubts that the few squirrels we saw, which were all on pasture land, had caused any real damage. I reminded him that in our tour of inspection we had seen golden eagles and considerable evidence of badgers and that he had told me his office had trapped coyotes a few months before on the same property. I pointed out that his office in its wholesale poisoning operations could well be tampering with an ecological equilibrium here that should remain undisturbed.

I also mentioned the indiscriminate killing of other, nontarget range rodents in the aerial spreading of the poison. "It has been my observation," I wrote, "that kangaroo rats, field mice and pocket gophers, acting as agents of soil development and rehabilitation, where occurring on range land such as was involved in this poisoning experiment, are more beneficial, in the long run, than detrimental."

We had found a poisoned magpie in our tour of inspection, which was probably an exception, as birds were not supposed to take the colored bait. Condors traditionally forage over this range, and I thought of other exceptions that could occur. I included in my letter the observation that kangaroo rats, when poisoned, generally die aboveground, with their pouches filled with the treated grain. Large raptorial birds, including condors, in feeding on these small rodents might swallow them whole, thus ingesting harmful amounts of the poisoned bait. In my letter I asked if there had been any research on this question.

After commenting on this new poisoning technique and other current matters of condor welfare, I told my two fellow condor watchers of another problem that had recently developed. In October of 1965, at the peak of his career, Alden Miller died of a heart attack. Suddenly condor preservation was without one of its great champions. At the time of his death Dr. Miller was chairman of an official Condor Survey Committee which had been recently organized to conduct an annual census of the condor population. The Survey Committee included representatives of the University of California, the United States Forest Service, the United States Fish and Wildlife Service, and the National Audubon Society, with the California Department of Fish and Game in general charge. I was a member because I had participated in the 1963–1964 condor survey.

In my view, this annual, two-day survey was vital to the success of the new condor program. If properly conducted the survey would recruit and develop a force of competent condor observers to work as organizers and missionaries of condor preservation. The survey would be a source of reliable, up-to-date condor information and would quickly direct attention to problems of condor welfare such as had previously passed unnoticed for years.

In October of 1966 the Second California Condor Survey was completed with 133 observers watching for condors at 65 locations throughout the species' range. The combined condor sightings for the last day of this survey were interpreted by a staff of wildlife technicians to represent 51 different condors. This was by far the highest figure yet reached for any single day of the two surveys. As an index to total numbers it seemed to indicate a population higher, even, than Koford's estimate of 60 birds in the 1940's. The 43 condors seen at one time by Perry Sprague on the Tejon Ranch in 1947 was Koford's highest index.

Certainly, everyone working to save the California condor hoped that the high count of 51 birds would prove to be well substantiated. But in meetings of the survey committee I had encountered a pronounced tendency toward exaggeration in reports of condors sighted. From my own examination of the data of the 1966 survey I could not find sufficient evidence to account for the 51 individuals reported. I could not even find proof that 25 condors had been seen, the highest number my brother and I had recorded at one time in our eighteen months of fieldwork in 1963 and 1964. If it was going to fulfill its promise as a dependable source of condor information the annual survey appeared to be in drastic need of correction. This needed correction was evidently in progress by the time of the third condor survey in the fall of 1967 when 46 condors were reported as the total number sighted.

I explained the 1966 survey to my two companions on this pilgrimage to the area of Kelly Truesdale's old nest and since they still appeared eager to hear more of the latest condor developments, I also told them about a big pen that was being constructed by the Fish and Wildlife Service to hold condors, and about a young California condor which had been captured a few months before in the fieldwork of the same agency and placed in a zoo in Los Angeles. I also told them about a meeting in which official plans had been laid for the keeping of other California condors that might be captured in the future.

At Alden Miller's death, Ben Glading, for almost three decades the chief of game management for the California Department of Fish and Game, had become chairman of the Condor Survey Committee. A year later, Carl Buchheister retired as president of the National Audubon Society. The new leadership of that organization was yet untried in matters of condor preservation. In one of its declarations of new policy it announced its endorsement of captive propagation as a means of preserving endangered species including wilderness species. This announcement came as the United States Fish and Wildlife Service, although having no legal authority over the California condor, was setting up a project to rear South American condors in captivity as preparation to do the same with the California species. This program of artificial condor propagation was financed with funds appropriated to expand the new, federal Endangered Species Program. Under this new regime zoo interests appeared to have quickly regained the influence they held in former years in matters of official condor management.

As I told the two young men about these new threats to the wild freedom of the condor, I pointed out the well-demonstrated capacity of the great birds to survive in the wild and how the current program for their natural preservation had every chance of producing an increase in the condor population, if at all properly carried out. I also explained the vital function of condor preservation as a cultural practice which developed and strengthened the human attributes needed in working out a new program for the welfare and survival of our own species.

At this point of our last look around our attention had passed along the southern horizon to the mile-high crest of Sierra Madre Ridge. In the two years since Eben and I had made our condor survey, the establishment of the San Rafael Wilderness Area had reached the final stages. This was a tremendous achievement both for general conservation and for the condors.

To its credit the Forest Service had changed its plans for developing peripheral parts of the area and was showing a more favorable attitude toward wilderness and the condor. Various trails in the more remote areas of Los Padres National Forest had been closed to motorized travel. Information about the condor and laws protecting the species was now available to anyone entering the forest. All of this, we agreed, deserved full acknowledgment and credit.

But the battle was not yet won. "Use" still appeared to be the dominating principle in the administration of Los Padres National Forest. Until almost the last moment the administration had attempted to exclude the crest of Sierra Madre Ridge and other areas bordering the upper rim of Sisquoc Canyon from the proposed wilderness area. These crucial outer ramparts that shield the Sisquoc condor country were still in danger from the development plan that would destroy the purpose of the wilderness area. Land clearing and road building were still going on on Sierra Madre Ridge.

Through our binoculars we could see stretches of the new public road that each year had extended farther from the west along the big ridge. We could also see the fields of planted pasturage. These distant marks of the bulldozer had come to symbolize Forest Service administration in the condor country.

As we discussed the bulldozer as the new symbol of land-use philosophy I noticed that the college student was keeping his binoculars focused on a particular point of the horizon. He said he was watching a speck in the sky low above the crest of Sierra Madre Ridge and that it appeared to be moving. Quickly I put my field glasses on this point and in a moment I saw the speck. It was moving and I could see it was a condor. For it moved in a way that only one kind of speck could move across the field of a pair of binoculars.

Bibliography

Burroughs, R. D. *The Natural History of the Lewis and Clark Expedition.* East Lansing, Mich.: Michigan State University Press, 1961.

Case, P. C., Barnes, W., and Rickel, L. *Management Plan for Sespe Wildlife Area.* U.S. Forest Service Document. 1952.

Dasmann, W. P. "Deer and National Forests," *Outdoor California,* Vol. XXIV (1963), 8–11.

Davis, J. "In memoriam: Alden Holmes Miller," *Auk,* Vol. LXXXIV (1967), 192–202.

Dawson, W. L. *The Birds of California.* Vol. IV. San Diego: South Moulton Co., 1923.

Finley, W. L. "Life History of the California Condor. Part 1," *Condor,* Vol. VIII (1906), 135–42.

Fisher, H. I. "The Skulls of Cathartid Vultures," *Condor,* Vol. XLVI (1944), 272–96.

Fisher, W. K. "When Joseph Grinnell and I Were Young," *Condor,* Vol. XLII (1940), 35–38.

Grinnell, H. W. "Joseph Grinnell: 1877–1939," *Condor,* Vol. XLII (1940), 3–34.

Grinnell, J. "Bird Life as a Community Asset," *California Fish and Game,* Vol. I (1914), 20–22.

——, Dixon, J. S., and Linsdale, J. M. *Fur-Bearing Mammals of California.* Vol. I. Berkeley: University of California Press, 1937.

Harris, H. "The Annals of Gymnogyps to 1900," *Condor,* Vol. XLIII (1941), 3–55.

Howard, H. "Trends in Avian Evolution," *Condor,* Vol. XLIX (1947), 10.

———. "Significance of Carbon-14 Dates for Rancho La Brea," *Science,* Vol. CXXXI, No. 3402 (1960), 712–14.

———. "Comparison of Avian Assemblages from Individual Pits at Rancho La Brea, California," *Contribution in Science,* No. 58 (Los Angeles County Museum, 1962), 1–24.

Koford, C. B. "A California Mountain Lion Observed Stalking," *Journal of Mammalogy,* Vol. XXVII (1946), 274–75.

———. *The California Condor, Research Report No. 4.* National Audubon Society, 1953.

Miller, A. H. "More Trouble for the California Condor," *Condor,* Vol. LV (1953), 47–48.

———. McMillan, I. I., and McMillan, E. *The Current Status and Welfare of the California Condor. Research Report No. 6.* National Audubon Society, 1965.

Miller, L. H. *Lifelong Boyhood.* Berkeley: University of California Press, 1950.

———. "Bird Remains from an Oregon Indian Midden," *Condor,* Vol. LIX (1957), 59–68.

———. "Birds and Indians in the West," *Bulletin Southern California Academy of Sciences,* Vol. LXII (1963), 178–91.

Robinson, C. S. "Notes on the California Condor Collected on Los Padres National Forest, California." Mimeographed, 1939.

Rudd, R. L. *Pesticides and the Living Landscape.* Madison, Wisc.: University of Wisconsin Press, 1964.

Smith, D., and Easton, R. *California Condor, Vanishing American.* Santa Barbara: McNally and Loftin, 1964.

Index